P9-DGF-855

WATERSHED

CANADA   Ontario

INTERIM
REPORT
AUGUST
1990

HONOURABLE
DAVID CROMBIE
COMMISSIONER

TORONTO, CANADA

Royal Commission on the Future
of the Toronto Waterfront

Royal Commission on the
Future of the
Toronto Waterfront

Commission royale sur
l'avenir du
secteur riverain de Toronto

Commissioner
The Honourable David Crombie, P.C.

Commissaire
L'honorable David Crombie, c.p.

Executive Director and Counsel
Ronald L. Doering

Directeur exécutif et Conseiller juridique
Ronald L. Doering

TO HIS EXCELLENCY
THE GOVERNOR GENERAL IN COUNCIL

MAY IT PLEASE YOUR EXCELLENCY

By Order in Council PC – 1988 – 589 dated March 30, 1988, I was
appointed Commissioner to inquire into and make recommendations regarding the future
of the Toronto Waterfront. I now beg to submit the attached Report.

Respectfully submitted.

David Crombie
Commissioner

August 1990

171, rue Slater St., 11th Floor/11ᵉ étage
P.O. Box/C.P. 1527
Station/Succursale "B"
Ottawa, Canada K1P 6P5

Tel. No./No. de téléphone: *(613)* 990–3306
Fax. No./No. de facsimilé: *(613)* 990–4345

207 Queen's Quay West/Ouest ,5th Floor/5ᵉ étage
P.O. Box/ C.P. 4111
Station/Succursale "A"
Toronto, Canada M5W 2V4

Tel. No./No. de téléphone: *(416)* 973–7185
Fax No./No.de facsimilé: *(416)* 973–7103

Royal Commission on the
Future of the
Toronto Waterfront

CANADA   Ontario

Commission royale sur
l'avenir du
secteur riverain de Toronto

Commissioner
The Honourable David Crombie, P.C.

Commissaire
L'honorable David Crombie, c.p.

Executive Director and Counsel
Ronald L. Doering

Directeur exécutif et Conseiller juridique
Ronald L. Doering

TO HIS HONOUR,
THE LIEUTENANT–GOVERNOR OF
THE PROVINCE OF ONTARIO

MAY IT PLEASE YOUR HONOUR:

By Order in Council O.C. 2465/89, dated the 12th day of October, 1989, I was duly appointed a Commissioner under the *Public Inquiries Act*. I am pleased to present to you the attached Report of the Royal Commission on the Future of the Toronto Waterfront.

Respectfully submitted.

David Crombie
Commissioner

August 1990

171, rue Slater St., 11th Floor/11ᵉ étage
P.O. Box/C.P. 1527
Station/Succursale "B"
Ottawa, Canada K1P 6P5

Tel. No./No. de téléphone: (613) 990–3306
Fax. No./No. de facsimilé: (613) 990–4345

207 Queen's Quay West/Ouest ,5th Floor/5ᵉ étage
P.O. Box/ C.P. 4111
Station/Succursale "A"
Toronto, Canada M5W 2V4

Tel. No./No. de téléphone: (416) 973–7185
Fax No./No.de facsimilé: (416) 973–7103

Commission Personnel

Executive Director and Counsel
Ronald L. Doering

Assistant to the Commissioner
Margaret Johnston

Senior Director, Special Projects
David Carter

Director, Port Studies
F. Shane Foreman

Director, Community Relations
Beverly Morley

Co-ordinator, Environmental Studies
Suzanne Barrett

Policy Analyst
Gordon Garland

Assistant to Counsel/Hearings Officer
Scott W. Clark

Assistant to the Senior Director, Special Projects
Deborah Williams

Librarian/Head of Registry
Monica Morrison

Systems Administrator
Marlaine Koehler

Administrative Assistants
Ginette Bellefeuille
Joan Lea

Publications Co-ordinator
Andrea Short

Editor
Sheila Kieran

French Editor
Margot Côté

Proofreader
David Kilgour

Support Staff

Wesley Birecki
Carolyn Chung
Anne Dixon
Janet Hollingsworth
Soo Kim

Vera Kubelikova
Charity Landon
Martha Lopez
Jean Sinclair
Jennifer Young

Secondees and Consultants

Max Beck
Paul Beck
Joe Berridge
Jim Bishop
Brian Denney
Gene Desfor
Noreen Dunphy
David L. Egar
Don Gamble
Lino Grima
David W. Guscott
Andy Hamilton
Neal Irwin
Beth Jefferson
Carol Ketchum
Joanna Kidd
Ken Lem
Simon Llewellyn
Rob Lockhart

Louise Madore-Payer
Jim Maxwell
Stephen McLaughlin
Christopher Morgan
Lynn Morrow
Paul Muldoon
Dan O'Halloran
Chuck Pautler
Ron Reid
Susan Richardson
Bob Shaw
Ron Shimizu
Peter Sly
Ray Spaxman
Laurel Spielberg
Mike Thorne
Rob Tonus
Bob Woodburn
Julian Woods
James Young

Table of Contents

Preface

On 1 June 1988, the Royal Commission on the Future of the Toronto Waterfront began its work as a federal inquiry, the Honourable David Crombie, Commissioner.

The Commission's mandate is to:

make recommendations regarding the future of the Toronto Waterfront, and to seek the concurrence of affected authorities in such recommendations, in order to ensure that, in the public interest, federal lands and jurisdiction serve to enhance the physical, environmental, legislative and administrative context governing the use, enjoyment and development of the Toronto Waterfront and related lands.

During its first year, the Commission published the reports of five working groups, as well as two research papers, one on the Toronto Harbour Commissioners and the other on the Toronto Island Airport. Its first *Interim Report* was released in August 1989.

From January to June 1989, the Commission held a series of public hearings on the major issues it was considering, at which it heard from nearly 300 deputants.

On 12 October 1989, the Government of Ontario, declaring that it "recognizes the importance of the Interim Report and recommendations of the ... Commission ..." appointed Mr. Crombie to carry on his duties on its behalf — thus making the Royal Commission on the Future of the Toronto Waterfront only the second federal-provincial royal commission in Canadian history. Moreover, the provincial government asked that he expand the Commission's area of study to include the waterfront from Burlington to Newcastle and north to the Oak Ridges Moraine — in other words, the Toronto watershed.

The Commission continued its vigorous publishing program and, by April 1990, had released a total of ten book-length reports, five working papers, five technical papers, the first *Interim Report*, and eight newsletters.

In April and May 1990, the Commission held three series of hearings, in Burlington and Oshawa as well as in the Commission's Toronto offices, to hear opinions and ideas from more than 100 groups and individuals.

The Commission has established the Canadian Waterfront Resource Centre, which now has a collection of more than 6,000 books, periodicals, pamphlets, and clippings. Subjects include: economic development, housing, the environment, public health, urban planning, transportation, parks, recreational facilities, and information about the ways in which Toronto and other communities, both in Canada and elsewhere, use their waterfront lands.

This report, *Watershed*, constitutes the Commission's second interim report. The Royal Commission on the Future of the Toronto Waterfront will soon release the work plan for its third year of operations and will publish its final report in the summer of 1991.

"A Pretty Average Day"

At five o'clock in the morning in early July, the rain began, slowly at first and then with increased intensity. It struck roof tops and trickled down gutters, gathered on driveways, parking lots, and roads. Along its way, the swirling stormwater picked up animal feces and herbicides from parks and yards, as well as asbestos, oil, and grease from roads. Before the rainfall ended, 4.5 billion litres of rainwater had gushed into the labyrinth of storm sewers under the metropolis.

At seven o'clock, people began to rise, taking showers, brushing teeth, and flushing toilets in 1.5 million households. By eight o'clock, when most had left for work or school, 770 million litres of wastewater had gone down household drains and into the sanitary sewer system. Combined storm and sanitary sewers were overflowing, and a noxious brew of stormwater and untreated sewage was flowing into local rivers or surging towards the sewage treatment plants. By nine o'clock, the hopelessly overburdened treatment plants began to bypass partially treated effluent directly into the nearshore of Lake Ontario.

Drivers sat in traffic with their windows closed, to avoid the exhaust from tailpipes, and listened to morning radio. "Heavier than usual traffic on the Don Valley southbound, the 401 westbound slow in both express and collector lanes," the announcers said.

Unseen by commuters, the brown and swollen rivers in the area disgorged their loads of sediments and toxic chemicals into Lake Ontario. At the river mouths, fishermen tossed their catches back into the lake, mindful of the signs that warned against eating fish. "Just a reminder to stay out of the water at area beaches for two days after this rainfall," the radio voices continued. By mid-morning, public health officials would be testing water at the beaches lining the waterfront; in less than a week, many would be closed to swimmers.

"Cloudy this morning, sunny later with highs of 25 degrees." Along with the afternoon sunshine would come high levels of eye-stinging smog. "And cooler temperatures tonight, especially near the lake. All in all," said the news readers, "a pretty average day in Greater Toronto."

CHAPTER ONE

ECOSYSTEM

Ecosystem

"Everything Is Connected To Everything Else"

Early in the work of the Royal Commission, it became apparent that the Toronto waterfront could not be viewed as simply a narrow band along the shore: it is linked by Lake Ontario to the other Great Lakes, by rivers and creeks to the watersheds, and by watermains, storm and sanitary sewers, and roads to homes and businesses throughout the Metropolitan area.

The air along the lakeshore is influenced by emissions from local and regional sources — automobiles and industries — and distant sources in the United States and beyond.

Beaches, dunes, shallow waters, wetlands, cliffs, woods, and meadows along the waterfront provide habitats for many species of resident and migrating wildlife. Some of these are linked to the hinterland through the movement of people and wildlife, via the river valleys, to Lake Ontario. Human uses of the land — transportation, housing, industry, business, and recreation — tie the waterfront economically and socially to the larger region in which it is located.

Human activities along the waterfront affect and are affected by areas outside it. Pollutants entering rivers upstream of the waterfront affect the water quality at river mouths. At the same time, organic chemicals discharged from storm sewers along the waterfront will influence water quality farther east in Lake Ontario and in the St. Lawrence River. In the same way, pollutants emitted into the air of the waterfront will have an impact downwind of the area.

These examples illustrate a fundamental point — everything is connected to everything else. They also pose challenges: how should we attempt to understand the ecosystem in which we live? How can we restore and protect it? The Commission believes that the best place to start is to adopt an ecosystem approach to all phases of activity —

studying, planning, remediating, protecting, and developing.

All ethics so far evolved rest upon a single premise; that the individual is a member of a community of interdependent parts. His instincts prompt him to compete for his place in that community, but his ethics prompt him also to co-operate (perhaps in order that there may be a place to compete for). The land ethic simply enlarges the boundaries of the community to include soils, waters, plants and animals, or collectively: the land. . . In short, a land ethic changes the role of *Homo sapiens* from conqueror of the land-community to plain member and citizen of it. It implies respect for his fellow members, and also respect for the community as such.

Leopold, A. 1949. "The land ethic." In *A Sand County almanac, and sketches here and there*, 203. Oxford: Oxford University Press.

The Ecosystem Approach

Ecosystem: "eco" from the Greek "oikos", meaning household, and "system", an interacting, interdependent complex.

The ecosystem concept is not new. The word was coined in 1935 by scientist Arthur Tansley, who defined it as a whole system that included not only the community of living organisms, but also the complex of physical factors forming the environment. Simply put, an ecosystem is composed of air, land, water, and living organisms, including humans, and the interactions among them. The concept has been applied to many types of interacting systems, including lakes, watersheds, cities, and the biosphere.

A healthy ecosystem is like a house of cards: carefully constructed and balanced, the cards support one another. If too many stresses are placed on it, the effect on the ecosystem is like that of removing too many cards from the house: the entire thing collapses.

A classic example in the Great Lakes Basin was the destruction of the Lake Erie fishery. The first sign of trouble during the 1950s was the disappearance of mayflies and their nymphs, food for many fish and birds. The cause was pollution of the water by excessive amounts of nutrients, especially phosphorus, from sewage and farm run-off. This enrichment fostered prolific growth of algae and other plants in the lake. When they died, the breakdown of the large quantities of plant matter by bacteria used up huge amounts of oxygen, and other

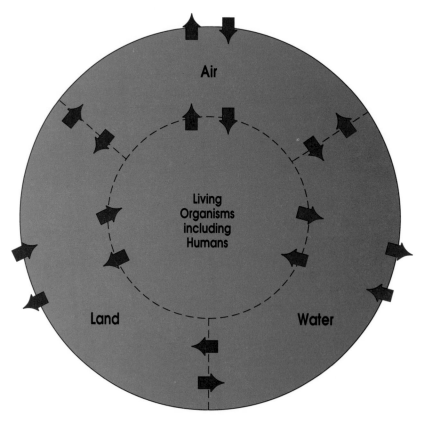

Air

Living
Organisms
including
Humans

Land

Water

Ecosystem

A hardwood forest

aquatic life, including the mayfly nymphs, suffocated.

The mayfly predators, including important commercial fish species such as perch, pickerel, cisco, and bass, declined dramatically. During the 1970s, concerted basin-wide efforts to reduce the inputs of phosphorus to Lake Erie gradually improved water quality. As a consequence, the mayflies have returned, and the fisheries have made a comeback.

The Lake Erie experience illustrates the critical interdependencies within ecosystems. Although current environmental problems may not be as easy to solve, the recovery of the Lake Erie fishery gives cause for hope that degraded ecosystems can be restored, if people understand the key relationships involved and deal effectively with root causes, rather than with symptoms.

Traditionally, human activities have been managed on a piecemeal basis, treating the economy separately from social issues or the environment. But the ecosystem concept holds that these are inter-related, that decisions made in one area affect all the others. To deal effectively with the environmental problems in any ecosystem requires a holistic or "ecosystem" approach to managing human activities.

> Two principles should guide conservation of intergenerational equity: the first is conservation of quality, defined as leaving the Great Lakes basin ecosystem in no worse condition than it was received from previous generations; the second is to conserve options, defined as conserving the diversity of the natural resource base of the Great Lakes.

1985. *The Great Lakes Water Quality Agreement: an evolving instrument for ecosystem management*, National Research Council and Royal Society of Canada. 109. Washington: National Academy Press.

There are some key characteristics of an ecosystem approach that help illustrate what is required. An ecosystem approach:

~ includes the whole system, not just parts of it;

~ focuses on inter-relationships among the elements;

~ understands that humans are part of nature, not separate from it;

~ recognizes the dynamic nature of the ecosystem — a moving picture rather than a still photograph;

~ incorporates the concepts of carrying capacity, resilience, and sustainability — suggesting that there are limits to human activity;

~ uses a broad definition of the environment — natural, physical, economic, social, and cultural;

~ encompasses both urban and rural activities;

~ is based on natural geographic units — such as watersheds — rather than on political boundaries;

~ embraces all levels of activity — local, regional, national, and international;

~ emphasizes the importance of living species other than humans and of generations other than our own;

~ is based on an ethic in which progress is measured by the quality, well-being, integrity, and dignity it accords natural, social, and economic systems.

Although widespread public recognition of the inter-related nature of environmental issues is relatively recent, scientists and institutions have been calling for the application of ecosystem thinking for some time.

For example, the Great Lakes Water Quality Agreement, signed by Canada and the United States in 1972, originally had a fairly narrow focus on the restoration of water quality. However, revisions and amendments to the Agreement in 1978 and 1987 provide a firm foundation for an ecosystem approach to the entire Great Lakes Basin. There was a recognition that "restoration and enhancement of the boundary waters cannot be achieved independently of other parts of the Great Lakes Basin Ecosystem with which these waters interact".

The Agreement promotes a view of humans as part of nature. It directs attention towards treatment of the whole patient (the ecosystem), rather than just to treatment of the symptoms of ill-health.

More recently (1989), a proposed Ecosystem Charter for the Great Lakes developed by the Rawson Academy of Aquatic Sciences recommended an approach to "management by people and their patterns of behaviour to assure greater compatibility with the natural systems of the region; a harmonizing of human activities with other parts of the ecosystem". This, it said, means "examination of the specific human activities that are behind the use and abuse of basin natural resources, and a new thinking in the design of sustainable developments in the future..."

Consistent with this thinking, the primary goal of the Metro Toronto Remedial Action Plan (RAP), as developed by the Public Advisory Committee (1989), is that:

Toronto's waterfront and watersheds should be a diverse, healthy, integrated ecosystem. They should be managed using an ecosystem approach in order to restore beneficial uses of our aquatic resources...

On a smaller scale, the environmental audit of the East Bayfront and Port Industrial Area being undertaken by the Royal Commission is based on an ecosystem approach. During Phase I of the audit, existing information was gathered on air, surface water, groundwater, soils, natural heritage, and built heritage (see Royal Commission Publication No.10: *East Bayfront and Port Industrial Area: Environment in Transition*). The review revealed a number of existing and potential links among processes and elements of the ecosystem. For example:

~ sources outside the study area contribute a great deal to the degradation of air, land, and water;
~ air quality problems (e.g., odours and suspended particulates) originating in the Port Industrial Area affect nearby communities (e.g., South Riverdale);
~ pollutants may be transferred from soils to buildings, affecting indoor air quality, and to ambient air in windblown dust and soil;
~ airborne contaminants (e.g., lead and salt from roadways) may be transferred to soils;
~ pollutants may migrate from groundwater to the surface waters of Lake Ontario;
~ food-chain contamination may result in accumulation of toxics in wildlife;
~ spatial links among open spaces/wildlife habitats (e.g., Cherry Beach, Leslie Street Spit, Toronto Islands, and the Don Valley) are poorly developed.

Phase II of the environmental audit will explore further these and other ecosystem relationships, in an attempt to address such questions as the following:

~ What are the implications of the environmental conditions in the area for human health, behaviour, activities, and access?
~ How are human activities affecting other elements of the ecosystem (air, land, water, and wildlife)?
~ What relationships exist among the environment of the study area and downtown Toronto, the Don Valley Watershed, the Greater Toronto Area, the Great Lakes Basin, etc.?
~ What measures are necessary to re-establish ecosystem integrity and to protect and restore beneficial uses?

Ecosystem under Stress: Greater Toronto Bioregion

The environmental audit is demonstrating the inextricable links among the East Bayfront/Port Industrial Area, other parts of Toronto, the Don River Watershed, and the Great Lakes. Similarly, the Greater Toronto Area waterfront being investigated by the Royal Commission is part of a region that includes the watersheds of the rivers leading into Lake Ontario from the GTA. Anything that happens within this area is tied ecologically to the health of the waterfront.

Therefore, in order to truly understand the waterfront itself, we must gain an understanding of the biological region, or bioregion, in which it lies.

We have defined the Greater Toronto Bioregion as the area bounded by the Niagara Escarpment on the west, the Oak Ridges Moraine to the north and east, and Lake Ontario to the south. The lands and waters in this bioregion share climatic and many ecological similarities. The soils and landforms are based on the glacial deposits of the Lake Ontario plain as it rises from the shores of the lake to meet the gravelly hills of the Oak Ridges Moraine. The watersheds arising in the moraine drain southwards to Lake Ontario and northwards to lakes Simcoe and Scugog. Most of the bioregion now falls within the commuter and economic orbit of Toronto. In this sense it is our home — the ecosystem in which we live, work, and play.

The defines of the bioregion are similar, but slightly smaller than those of the GTA, which includes the regions of Halton, Peel, Metro Toronto, York, and Durham. This description of the condition of the bioregion includes some information from the GTA itself, simply because such information exists. Nevertheless, it must be remembered that the area described is circumscribed by natural, not political, boundaries. It is currently under considerable stress from human activities.

The authors of *Great Lakes, Great Legacy?*, published by Washington's Conservation Foundation and Ottawa's Institute for Research on Public Policy, usefully categorize the many types of stress that can affect ecosystem health.

~ First, there are natural processes: weather, fire, and disease outbreaks.

~ Second, there is the addition (loading) of substances to the environment; in the Greater Toronto Bioregion, it includes the erosion of soil into bodies of water, the addition of nutrients like nitrogen and phosphorus into lakes, and the emission of chemical and heavy metals into air, water or soil.

~ Third, physical restructuring — e.g., damming and diking of rivers and streams, dredging of harbours, clearing of forests, drainage of wetlands, and altering shorelines with structures such

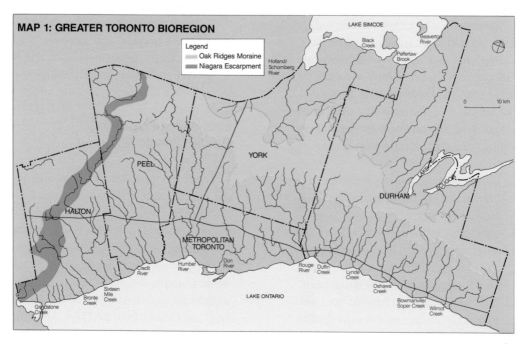

MAP 1: GREATER TORONTO BIOREGION

Lake Shore Boulevard and the Keating Channel

as seawalls or lakefilling — places stress on the ecosystem.

~ The fourth category of ecosystem stress is the removal of renewable and non-renewable resources, including withdrawal of ground or surface waters, commercial forestry, fishing, and the extraction of minerals and aggregate.

~ Finally, the introduction of non-native organisms is also stressful. Most notable in the Great Lakes was the unwitting introduction of the sea lamprey when the St. Lawrence Seaway was completed; most recently, the arrival of the zebra mussel from Europe threatens the lakes.

All these stresses are at work in the Greater Toronto Bioregion. In order to provide a thumbnail sketch of the area's condition, we examine it using an ecosystem approach. Although there are many gaps in information, the following provide some revealing information about the characteristics of land, human activity, water, air, and wildlife in the bioregion.

The Hooded Merganser

Land

Two great forces — one natural and one human — have shaped the Greater Toronto Bioregion as we know it today. The greatest natural force shaping the area was the retreat, starting about 15,000 years ago, of the Wisconsin Glaciers. As they slowly withdrew to end the last ice age, the glaciers carved out the rivers flowing north to Lake

Simcoe, east to Lake Scugog, and south to Lake Ontario, and they left behind the fertile soils characteristic of much of the area.

In the northern part of the bioregion, the retreating glaciers left in their path the hilly Oak Ridges Moraine, a unique formation of sand and gravel deposits. For thousands of years, rainwater has filtered downwards through the moraine, migrated laterally, and then discharged upwards to form wetlands — the headwaters of virtually all the rivers flowing south and north in the area. As the ice age loosened its frigid grip and temperatures rose, river valleys were flooded and fertile marshes developed at river mouths. Natural forces left us a unique, varied, and complex bioregion.

The second great force shaping the Greater Toronto Bioregion has been human habitation. Although settlement likely began about 11,000 years ago, humans had little impact on the area until the arrival of Europeans in the 18th and 19th centuries. Settlement first occurred along the water's edge, because Lake Ontario provided water to drink and fish and waterfowl for the table. Moreover, water was a highway: with dense and seemingly impenetrable forests hindering road building, all goods and people had to be transported by water.

However, once the boreal and Carolinian forests were cleared for agricultural use, settlement soon crept northwards, rivers were dammed, and towns and roads were built. Subsequent industrialization and urbanization dramatically altered the physical form of the bioregion: recent satellite photos show clearly the urbanized areas that stretch ever-north from the shores of Lake Ontario, and the network of roads, rail lines, and hydro corridors that criss-cross the region to service its needs.

Today, about 25 per cent of the Greater Toronto Area is covered by cities and towns. Despite extensive (and intensive) urbanization, significant environmental diversity remains: about half the land base can still be categorized as "agricultural" or "rural"

in nature, although not all of this rural land is farmed. More than 216,000 people live in the rural areas of the GTA, but as few as 15,000 are involved in farming. Nonetheless, there are some 5,000 farms in the GTA, and in 1986, these farms produced eight per cent of the agricultural goods sold in Ontario.

At the same time, loss of farmland in the GTA has been significant: federal statistics show that, between 1981 and 1986, about eight per cent of the total agricultural acreage — much of it prime agricultural land — was lost. With continued expansion of urban populations, the pressures on agricultural land can be expected to increase in the future.

Despite the widespread clearing of forests over the last 200 years, one-fifth of the GTA — including parks, Crown land, and private woodlots — remains forest-covered today. There is disturbing evidence, however, that these trees and their urban cousins are under significant stress from drought, salt, and pollutants such as acid rain. Conditions facing newly planted trees in Metro Toronto are so harsh that in some areas their life span is estimated to be no more than ten years.

Glacial deposits of sand and gravel in the bioregion provide extensive aggregate resources — a fifth of all that produced in the province. It is no small irony, however, that the areas richest in aggregates — the Niagara Escarpment and the Oak Ridges Moraine — are the most sensitive to its extraction. Aggregate extraction on the escarpment threatens its integrity as a unique landform, while that in the moraine interferes with its hydrogeological function as the site of headwaters of rivers.

There are 16 major rivers flowing into Lake Ontario in the Greater Toronto Bioregion, and approximately 65 river valley systems in the area. Although few of the river valley systems are in a totally natural state, they continue to fulfil important functions for human activity (including recreation) and as corridors or links for the movement of wildlife.

Wetlands provide rich habitats for wildlife, and act as nature's filters to clean surface waters. It is only recently that the importance of wetlands in ecosystems has been recognized, long after human settlement has dramatically altered the number and quality of wetlands in Ontario. It is estimated that as many as 2.4 million hectares (5.9 million acres) of southern Ontario were originally covered by wetlands, and that 70 to 80 per cent of these have been severely altered or destroyed. It is also estimated that more than half the wetlands and marshes in the GTA have already been lost, and today, only one significant coastal marsh — Rattray Marsh— exists in the long stretch between Toronto and Burlington.

In more than 200 years of human activity, wetlands have been drained for farms, bulldozed for housing, or infilled to provide land for industrial or transportation use. Many of today's remaining wetlands in the bioregion have been degraded as the result of upstream pollution or surrounding land uses, and are subject to intense pressure by increased urbanization.

Human influences have extensively altered the geography of the shoreline of Lake Ontario from Burlington to Newcastle. A network of highway and rail corridors runs along the waterfront's edge, while the underwater contours of the lake have been altered by stonehooking (the collection of rock for building) and dredging. Lakefilling programs dating back to the end of the 19th century have filled marshes, created harbours, and been used to establish recreational parks.

In Toronto, for example, all the land south of The Esplanade was created by lakefilling for port and transportation use. Toronto's Port Industrial Area is built on land reclaimed from the Ashbridge's Bay marsh, which was at the mouth of the Don River. The Leslie Street Spit (Tommy Thompson Park), which stretches southward from the Port Industrial Area, was created by the Toronto Harbour Commissioners, using fill

Our deepest folly is the notion that we are in charge of the place, that we own it and can somehow run it. We are beginning to treat the earth as a sort of domesticated household pet, living in an environment invented by us, part kitchen garden, part park, part zoo. It is an idea we must rid ourselves of soon, for it is not so. It is the other way around. We are not separate beings. We are a living part of the earth's life, owned and operated by the earth, probably specialized for functions on its behalf that we have not yet glimpsed.

Thomas, L. 1985. In *Dwellers in the land: the bioregional vision*, K. Sale. 191. San Francisco: Sierra Club.

over a period of 30 years, originally to provide an expansion of harbour facilities. The Metropolitan Toronto and Region Conservation Authority has created four parks from lakefill, and has plans to create two more.

Such parks create recreational space for humans and habitat for wildlife, especially

Transportation corridor, Metro Toronto

Saw-whet Owl

fish, but not without cost to the environment. One concern is the impact on water quality from contaminants in the fill, and chemicals and metals in sediments that are resuspended during the lakefilling process itself. Another worry is that lakefill adversely affects coastal processes — the currents that move and deposit sand, and which, if unimpeded, naturally cleanse the shorelines of pollutants. Finally, such alterations to the natural shoreline have degraded, and in many places destroyed, valuable wildlife habitats.

In some places, the soils of the bioregion contain chemical pollution, the legacy of

The environment and the economy must be put on an equal footing, to be weighed and measured together as the basis for development decisions. This will require governments, industry, and individuals alike to integrate environmental and economic decision making.

1990. *Great Lakes, great legacy?*, T. E. Colborn, A. Davidson, S. N. Green, R. A. Hodge, I. C. Jackson and R. A. Liroff. 230. Baltimore: The Conservation Foundation and the Institute for Research on Public Policy.

human industrial activities. Studies have shown, for example, that the soils of Toronto's Central Waterfront — in many cases the same areas that were created by lakefilling — contain heavy metals and organic chemicals deposited over 100 years of unwittingly careless transportation, industrial activity, lakefilling, and waste dumping.

The extent of soil contamination in areas of historical industrial use elsewhere in the region is not known, although the City of Toronto has been preparing an inventory of old industrial sites where contamination may have taken place. The Royal Commission's audit of Toronto's Port Industrial Area indicates the types of industry where soil contamination is likely to be found; one such category is old refineries — and there are half a dozen old refineries along the Greater Toronto Waterfront.

Although technology exists to clean up contaminated soils, the cost of remediation is high. What is less clear is the environmental costs of not cleaning them up.

More information exists about historical solid waste landfills than about soil contamination at old industrial sites: as many as 276 abandoned landfill sites dot the GTA. However, because waste dumping was essentially unregulated until about 20 years ago, it is difficult to say what materials were deposited in any particular landfill and there is little information about the extent of soil and groundwater contamination that may be occurring around such sites.

Human Activity

The land base of the Greater Toronto Bioregion represents about one per cent of Ontario, and is home to about four million people — fully 40 per cent of Ontario's population. The GTA population is one-third greater than that of British Columbia, and almost twice that of Alberta. The number of people living in the area began to increase dramatically in the post-war industrial boom. In the 25 years between 1961 and 1986, for example, the GTA's population grew by 1.6 million people, a rate of about nine per cent per annum — three times that in the rest of the province.

Significant numbers of people continue to be attracted to the area — net migration is about 60,000 people a year (the equivalent of the population of Kingston). More than half of all immigrants coming to Canada end up in the GTA. Although the rates of migration and population growth are expected to slow in future, the population of the GTA is expected to increase to as much as 5.4 million by 2011, mostly in the regions outside Metro Toronto.

In 1986, the population on the Greater Toronto Waterfront (defined as the first two census tracts north of the water's edge) was about 366,000 people, or roughly ten per cent of the total population of the GTA. Redevelopment and changes in land use have meant significant growth in housing on the waterfront since 1987 — from 1987 to 1989, a total of 7,860 housing units were built on the waterfront. Only 15 per cent of them were assisted or market rental units, the balance being homeowner condominium units, mostly one-bedrooms and bachelors. The result has been an imbalance in waterfront housing starts between condo and other housing types — an imbalance that, to a large degree, excludes families and moderate-income households.

The population explosion in the GTA has been both a causal factor and a consequence of the substantial economic growth in the bioregion. The GTA has been called the "economic engine that drives the nation", and is currently the fastest-growing urban area in North America. Home to about 16 per cent of the nation's population, the area generates about 20 per cent of its personal income. The region generated some $100 billion of Gross Provincial Product (GPP) in 1988, two-thirds of that of Quebec and 25 per cent larger than that of British Columbia. Half the income tax paid to the federal and provincial governments from Ontario comes from the GTA.

In the Toronto Census Metropolitan Area (CMA), which is smaller than the GTA, unemployment rates in 1988 and 1989 were less than half the national average. The Toronto CMA remains the manufacturing capital of Canada and also offers substantial numbers of jobs in a variety of sectors: business, personal, and community services; trade and commerce; finance, insurance, and real estate; and transportation, communications, and utilities.

Keeping the GTA economic engine running requires large amounts of energy: transportation and heating; and residential, institutional, and industrial cooling and lighting, which require 275 gigajoules of energy per capita per year (the equivalent of 8,000 litres of gasoline). Some electricity is generated in the GTA, notably at the Lakeview Generating Station in Mississauga and the Pickering Nuclear Plant. In general, however, the area imports more electricity

The Niagara Escarpment, Mount Nemo Conservation Area

In fact, employment growth in the area has been strong since 1981 and, by 1986, there were 2.1 million jobs in the GTA. Some 370,000 jobs were created between 1983 and 1989 and predictions are that employment growth will continue to increase and will reach 3.5 million jobs by 2031. Most growth is expected to occur by the turn of the century and, as in the case of population growth, is expected to occur in the regions outside Metro Toronto — unless population patterns change.

from distant hydro-electric and nuclear sources than it produces.

Although there are some petroleum refineries in the GTA, all the crude oil and natural gas used comes from outside the area and is transported into it by tanker truck or pipeline. In sum, the GTA is a net energy importer, and to a large degree, the environmental costs of energy production are borne elsewhere.

Canadians produce more solid waste (garbage) per capita than any other people

Autumn in the Oak Ridges Moraine

in the world. The four million residents of the GTA produce about 4.5 million tonnes of waste annually — more than a tonne per person. Forty per cent of that waste comes from homes; the rest is produced by institutions, industries or commercial establishments. The amount being recycled ranges from eight to about 20 per cent across the GTA, with the remainder taken to landfill disposal sites, most of which are in the GTA. (The exception is the Region of Halton, which has no landfill site, and which ships its garbage to St. Catharines and Niagara Falls, New York for disposal.) The regions of the GTA face a major garbage crisis: landfill capacity for the area will be exhausted by mid-1993. The five regions joined together in 1989 to explore development of a long-term waste management system for the GTA.

It is not known how much hazardous waste, which, according to provincial regulations, must be specially treated, is produced by the 6,000 industries and commercial establishments in the GTA. The GTA, however, has no facilities for the special treatment of hazardous wastes, and such wastes are sent for treatment and disposal to facilities in Quebec, Sarnia, and the United States. Small quantities of hazardous wastes are exempted from government regulation, and are often dumped into sewage treatment systems of the GTA.

Because sewage treatment plants (STPs) are not designed to deal with organic chemicals and heavy metals, much of this toxic load ends up in the waters of Lake Ontario. The precise amount coming from industry is unknown, and there are substantial (though unknown) quantities of "household hazardous waste" — cleaners, pesticides, solvents, and paints — being poured down residential sinks in the area.

Four million people also produce a lot of human waste and a vast amount of wastewater. Across the bioregion, a network of sewers collects and transports this wastewater to 11 STPs for treatment. The network is vast — Metro alone has 336 kilometres (210 miles) of sewers — and, especially in older areas, repairs or replacement of crumbling and leaking pipes are needed. Some sewage treatment plants are under-sized and expansion of capacity at Metro's Main STP, in order to meet existing and future needs, is expected to cost $1.5 billion. Almost half of the flow into Lake Ontario in the Toronto area comes through the sewage treatment plants (the rest is from rivers in the area) and the plants are responsible for high loadings of nutrients to the nearshore areas of Lake Ontario.

A typical rainfall in the Toronto area dumps approximately 4.5 billion litres (one billion gallons) of water that rushes off roofs, roads, and parking lots into sewers,

and often into combined storm and sanitary sewer lines. This sudden pulse of water can cause several problems: stormwater, already contaminated with animal droppings, oil,

The heart of the Central Business District, City of Toronto

grease, metals, and other contaminants, mixes with untreated human sewage. The noxious brew enters the rivers in the area or descends on sewage treatment plants designed to carry only some of the extra burden. In order to prevent flooding at the plants, the sewage/stormwater mixture is given only partial treatment and is diverted into the lake. The resulting high level of bacteria is largely responsible for the beach closings along the Greater Toronto Waterfront every summer.

One solution to the problem of combined sewers is to separate them into sewage lines and stormwater lines. In Metro, this work has been under way in the various municipalities for many years, but the task remains

to be completed. The City of Toronto, for example, is farthest along in separating combined sewers, but even it needs between one and three billion dollars to finish the job. And even that will not satisfy the need for infrastructure: separating combined sewers probably means that facilities will have to be established to store and/or treat the stormwater, which is very dirty.

The cities of Toronto and York are starting to build stormwater detention tanks to address this problem, but a comprehensive solution is years — perhaps decades — away.

Over the last ten to 15 years, transportation demand in the GTA has far outstripped supply; the construction of new roads, transit services, terminals, and parking facilities has not kept up with the demand for these services. Existing facilities are strained to

Upstream in Sixteen Mile Creek, Milton, Ontario

the limit: Highway 401 usage is currently 25 per cent above the capacity for which it was designed; runways and terminals at Pearson International Airport are overcrowded; parts of the GO Transit system are operating at greater than 120-per-cent seating capacity; and parts of the Toronto subway system are at effective capacity. The results are readily apparent: congestion on roads, more frequent and longer delays, more stress being felt by people, increased air pollution, and inefficient energy use.

Asked by the City of Toronto Planning Department recently to list their ten main dislikes about the City, frustrated residents identified traffic congestion as their first concern.

Toronto recently received the dubious honour of being named the most expensive city in the western hemisphere. In part, this is due to the cost of housing. In 1989, the price of the average house sold in the Toronto CMA was $274,000, the highest in Canada. Elsewhere in Canada, house prices were substantially lower, ranging from $76,000 in Saskatoon to $210,000 in Greater Vancouver.

Metro continues to have one of the country's tightest rental markets, with apartment vacancy rates around 0.2 per cent, or two available units per thousand. Most new housing being built outside Metro takes the form of single family dwellings or condominiums. Meanwhile, about 190,000 households in the GTA are deemed by the federal government to be in "core housing need": there are members of approximately 27,800 households in the GTA on government waiting lists for subsidized housing, and countless others wait for space in non-profit and co-op housing projects.

Among the obvious casualties of the lack of affordable housing are the growing numbers of homeless people — the City of Toronto's *Healthy Toronto 2000* report estimates that they number between 10,000 and 25,000 in that city alone. Food banks have become a fixture across the GTA in the last few years, and studies indicate that the problem is shelter-related: they show that the average food bank user spends 70 per cent of his or her income on a place to live. Clearly, a substantial number of people are not sharing the benefits of the GTA's "economic engine".

Water

The Great Lakes Basin, which is the centre of the industrial heartland of both Canada and the United States, has been called the most polluted part of North America — an alarming designation for the source of the drinking water of half of Canada's population.

As the last in the string of Great Lakes, downstream of the other four, Lake Ontario has to contend with problems originating in them — in addition to the problems generated along its own shores. In 1985, the International Joint Commission, concerned about the degraded state of the basin and in order to make people aware of the need to take action, designated 42 areas around the Great Lakes Areas of Concern or "hot spots".

Metro Toronto's waterfront is one of them; others nearby include Port Hope and Hamilton Harbour. The intention is to develop remedial plans in order to restore water quality. In co-operation with the U.S. and various state governments, the Government of Canada and the provinces of Ontario and Quebec are also developing a lake-wide remedial plan, the Lake Ontario Toxics Management Plan. Initiatives are being developed under the terms of the bilateral Great Lakes Water Quality Agreement, which is based on the ecosystem approach and the goal of "zero discharge of persistent toxic chemicals".

When European settlers first arrived in the Toronto area a little more than 200 years ago, the bay on which it was situated was of "beautifully clear and transparent water". The bay and the nearby Ashbridge's Marsh provided residents with fish, turtles, waterfowl, and wild rice for their tables. But the impact of human presence on water quality began to be felt as early as 1840, at which time the water quality in the harbour and nearby areas was already moderately to severely degraded, due primarily to the dumping of untreated sewage from the City.

By the end of the 19th century, the residents of Toronto viewed the marshlands of Ashbridge's Bay as a "malarial swamp... teeming with pestilence and disease"; in fact, the sad condition of the bay was a prime factor in the Toronto Harbour Commissioners' decision, in 1911, to fill it in.

The development of sewage treatment systems in the early part of the 20th century dramatically reduced the loadings of sewage and immediately improved the health of the City's inhabitants. Today, however, a host of nutrients, sediments, organic chemicals,

Lower Morningside, a Rouge River tributary

Sunnyside Beach warning, June 1990

and heavy metals still reach the waterfront via the rivers in the area, storm and combined sewers, and sewage treatment plant discharges and bypasses.

The International Joint Commission designated the Metropolitan Toronto Waterfront an Area of Concern because of chemical and bacterial contamination. Problems include:

~ bottom sediments contaminated by bacteria, metals, PCBs, and other chemicals;

~ bioaccumulation of metals and organics by organisms living in the sediments;

~ fish of some species with such high levels of contaminants they cannot be eaten safely by humans;

~ an aquatic community under stress from sewage treatment plant outfalls, poor water circulation, changes in water temperature, habitat destruction, and chemical contamination; and

~ beaches that must be closed throughout the summer.

In addition, Metro residents are concerned about the quality of their drinking water. Both Metro and the Ontario Ministry of the Environment regularly monitor Toronto's tap water for a wide range of metals, organics, pesticides, and other potential contaminants. Although the water meets existing standards, nearly one-quarter of all Toronto households use alternate sources such as bottled water or water filters. The cost of these, per litre, has been calculated to be 600 times the cost of municipally supplied water.

In order to address the pollution problems on Metro's waterfront, the provincial and federal governments are co-ordinating development of a Remedial Action Plan (RAP) to restore water quality. The RAP is looking at the waterfront from Etobicoke Creek in the west to the Rouge River in the east, together with all the watersheds draining the area.

Bypasses of sewage treatment plants during heavy rainfalls contribute to high bacterial counts on the waterfront, and are part of the reason beaches are closed in summer. But even more disturbing, the plants themselves contribute about 90 per cent of the organic chemicals and heavy metals that enter the Greater Toronto Waterfront.

The problem of sewer dumping of toxic chemicals is expected to be dealt with under the Province's Municipal-Industrial Strategy for Abatement (MISA) program. The goal of MISA is to "stop pollution at the source", both from direct dischargers in eight major industrial sectors (none of which are on the Greater Toronto Waterfront) and from municipal sewage treatment plants and systems. Industrial and commercial users of the sewage systems — an estimated 3,000 in the Toronto area — will have to meet tough standards for sewer discharge of toxic chemicals when the new MISA regulations are enacted in 1994.

The Greater Toronto Bioregion is rich in rivers — 16 major rivers and dozens of minor tributaries run through it — but their condition varies considerably, with few of them in a truly healthy state. In many cases, lower reaches have been straightened or encased in concrete. Forest cutting has removed shade and banks have eroded. Pesticides, fertilizers, and topsoil from farms, as well as a host of rain-washed pollutants from urban areas, flow into the rivers. Because of combined sewer overflows, these rivers are the major source of waterfront bacteria.

A ranking of rivers according to their ecological health shows that only a few streams in forested areas of the Oak Ridges Moraine can be considered in excellent condition, while streams in urbanized areas are of "fair" or "poor" quality and, in some cases, do not support any fish at all.

Toronto's once-beautiful Don River is a graphic example of severe degradation, and has been described as an "open sewer". Until the 1850s, salmon could still be speared in the Don, near Castle Frank (close to the present-day Bloor Viaduct). Even 70 years later, much of the valley was still a wilderness, and the noted writer and historian Charles Sauriol tells us:

> The Forks of the Don in the '20s and '30s was sylvan, serene and naturally beautiful. Huge graceful elms stood along the river banks and on the flood plain, over which cattle roamed. Some of the Valley slopes were covered with white pine, long since replaced with the deciduous trees of today...Three streams met at the Forks: the West Don, the East Don and Taylor Creek.

The wholeness of nature that encompasses the very structure of every living thing dictates that all forms of life, from frog's eggs to maple trees to humans, are linked in our requirements for life. We, the living entities of this planet, all ask the same things of the biosphere, that thin shell of air, water, and soil that surrounds our globe and supports life. If we alter conditions of the biosphere too far, we, and other species, will all fail together.

Theberge, J. B. 1989. "The wholeness of nature." In *Legacy: the natural heritage of Ontario*, editor J. B. Theberge. 375. Toronto: McClelland and Stewart.

Huddled in the folds of the Valley and tracing the old course of the East Don were several frog ponds.

Today the Don Valley Parkway winds its way alongside a dirty, diminished river, into which is drained the outpouring of some 1,185 storm sewers, 30 combined sewer overflows, several industrial coolant discharges, and the treated effluent from the North Toronto Sewage Treatment Plant.

While the condition of the Don today is undeniably bad, the river has also come to symbolize what can be done if governments, the private sector, and the public embark on the complex process of clean-up. Restoring the Don will mean cleaning up the entire watershed — otherwise, it would be impossible. A restored Don River would be an indicator of a bioregion on its way to a restored ecosystem.

While the problems of water quality along Metro Toronto's waterfront are more severe than in neighbouring areas, they are typical of the water quality near most cities: contaminated sediments, consumptive uses, chemical and metal pollution coming through sewage treatment plants, closed beaches, degraded wildlife habitat, and contaminants in aquatic biota occur throughout the Great Lakes.

Individual action can make a substantial difference to some of these: for example, avoiding the use of hazardous household products can improve water quality, as can water conservation. Other problems — chemicals in sewage treatment plants, for example — must be addressed at source (at the industrial plant) and regulated at the regional level. Still others — such as the persistent chemicals like PCBs that bioaccumulate in living tissues — can be remedied only as the result of provincial, national, and international co-operation.

In future, water quantity may be as much an issue as water quality. Consumption of water near the Great Lakes has risen dramatically in the last few decades: in 1985, the International Joint Commission predicted that, if current rates of withdrawal continue, levels in the upper lakes would drop slightly by the year 2000. A more significant drop in levels would have a drastic effect on shipping and power generation.

Unfortunately, there is little understanding of the need for water conservation in the GTA — and why should there be? After all, there is a huge lake out there and Canadians believe, incorrectly, that we have enormous resources of fresh water. Moreover, water use is not being metered in 70 per cent of the houses in the GTA, which means that users pay a flat rate, irrespective of how much they use, and have little incentive to conserve.

Nor are quantity problems restricted to the communities that draw their water from Lake Ontario: some municipalities in York and Peel regions, where demand has increased substantially in the past decade, still depend on groundwater that has been stored in deep underground aquifers for as long as 4,000 years. The water in these aquifers is recharged, or gradually replaced by water from the Oak Ridges Moraine, and there is concern that valuable groundwater resources may be depleted. As a result, communities such as Aurora have initiated water conservation programs.

Air

The study of ecology has taught us that it is not possible to draw lines around a geographic area — the environment simply does not respect borders, whether they are local, regional or national. This is especially true of the atmospheric environment, which is defined as including the quality of both outside and inside air, noise, and radiation.

Ambient (or outside) air quality can be affected by local, regional or distant factors; local factors include nearby sources of air pollutants — industries or automobiles. Those that are regional include topography (the actual shape of the land), and other features or conditions that affect meteorology.

Along the waterfront, for example, the presence of Lake Ontario helps disperse pollutants. Distant factors that may affect air quality include the long-range transport of pollutants from other countries.

The atmospheric region of influence, or airshed, for the Greater Toronto Bioregion has been defined as stretching as far as Hudson Bay to the north, New Brunswick to the east, the Dakotas to the west, and central Georgia to the south. Therefore, the residents of Greater Toronto have limited control over the quality of the air they breathe.

In the ecosystem defined as the Greater Toronto Bioregion, the links between air, water, land, human activity, and wildlife are complex. Air quality can affect, and be affected by, pollutants in soil and water.

The mouth of the Don River and the Keating Channel

Organic chemicals in soils, for example, can become volatile and heavy metals become resuspended when disturbed. Dust, small particles, heavy metals, and other pollutants in air can be deposited in soil and vegetation, while contaminants in the air can be deposited in water.

Studies of Lake Superior show that the major inputs of the pesticide toxaphene — long-banned in Canada and the United States, but still used in Central and South America — come via long-range air transport. The Ontario regulations governing air pollution are intended to protect the "most sensitive receptor"; in some cases, that most sensitive receptor is a human being, while, in others, it is a building or a species of vegetation. The regulatory framework, however, is not geared to deal with the transfer of contaminants from one medium to another (i.e., from air to water or water to soil).

In the 1970s, sulphur dioxide and particulates were Toronto's worst pollutants, and control of them was the basis of the Province's Air Pollution Index. The index was

to natural gas. Levels of sulphur dioxide are not a problem for human health in the bioregion, but are still a concern because of its role in the formation of acid rain downwind.

Ten-year trends indicate a steady decline in levels of suspended particulate, carbon monoxide, and the most commonly monitored metals — copper and lead. This contrasts with the presence of nitrogen dioxide and volatile organic compounds, which have

Grazing pasture near Town of Newcastle

designed as an alert-and-control system to signal deteriorating air quality by measuring the levels of sulphur dioxide and suspended particulates in the air, high concentrations of which have been linked to respiratory disease. Since 1985, however, there has been only one Air Pollution Advisory issued in the Greater Toronto Area; in general, levels of sulphur dioxide have dropped steadily in the past ten years because of regulatory control of the sulphur content of coal and gas used in Toronto, and because of a move from coal

remained fairly constant and at high levels. Improved control of the main sources of these pollutants — automobiles, power plants, and certain industries — has been offset by the increased numbers of automobiles on the street. While levels *per se* do not pose a problem for human health, they contribute to acid rain and are important precursors of the formation of ground-level ozone.

Ground-level ozone is the prime ingredient of eye-stinging urban smog. High concentrations at ground level can damage vegeta-

The Finch Meander, Rouge River

**That is the true measure of a city —
the well-being of its people. Their
opportunities, the quality of life they
lead, the air they breathe. At the
end of the day, I would be much
prouder to have Toronto known
as a 'healthy city' than a 'world-
class city'.**

Eggleton, A. 9 June 1990. In "Toronto: it's pricey
but livable: survey gives us edge over Montreal,
five U.S. cities." *Toronto Star* D1.

tion and harm human health. Ozone is formed
downwind of originating sources through a
complicated series of reactions involving
nitrogen dioxides and volatile organic compounds in the presence of sunlight. Over the
past ten years, levels of ozone have remained
essentially constant, and are fairly uniform
across Southern Ontario. They are highest
in the City of Toronto, where they regularly
exceed the federal standard of 120 parts
per billion.

In October 1989, the City of Toronto's
Special Advisory Committee on the Environment recommended a comprehensive
strategy to reduce automobile emissions. This
included improvements to public transit and
aggressive management of automobile use in

the City, as well as suggestions that the federal government strengthen automobile fuel efficiency standards and adopt California's tough emission standards for nitrogen oxides and hydrocarbons.

The fact that concentrations of ozone are highest in warm, sunny weather, when winds carry ozone-laden air north from the United States to the north shore of Lake Ontario, is a reminder that we are part of an ecosystem: while U.S. sources are largely responsible for our smog problems, the pollutants generated here will be carried off on the winds to cause ozone problems elsewhere.

Another class of air pollutants for which distant sources appear to be largely responsible is toxic organic compounds — those that can affect health, even at extremely low concentrations. Among such compounds are dioxins and furans, as well as a host of industrial and agricultural chemicals. As yet, however, the magnitude of the problem has been neither well defined nor addressed comprehensively by governments.

However, in order to study the type and concentrations of trace organic compounds in the air, the Ontario Ministry of the Environment has recently established a monitoring station on the Toronto Islands. There, levels of these compounds are found to be similar to those at rural monitoring stations throughout Ontario, which suggests that distant sources are responsible for much of the toxic organic compounds found in the air.

In recent years, atmospheric scientists have warned about the dangers of global warming — the "greenhouse effect". Trends to global warming are attributed to the emission into the environment of greenhouse gases, including carbon dioxide, methane, nitrous oxide, ground-level ozone, and chlorofluorocarbons (CFCs). There are predictions that by 2050, if emission of these gases goes unchecked, temperatures will rise as much as 4.5 degrees celsius above those of the late 1880s. On a global scale, this kind of increase is expected to result in more frequent and serious droughts, extensive desertification of some areas, forest dieback, and rising sea levels.

Recognizing that these problems are global in scale, the City of Toronto recently adopted recommendations made by the Special Advisory Committee on the Environment in its 1989 report, *The Changing Atmosphere: A Call to Action*. It recommended urgent action at the local level, including preventive measures (a reduction in emissions and increased energy efficiency of buildings), reforestation projects to offset and recycle carbon emissions, and measures to adapt locally to climatic change.

Recent news reports about the thinning of the ozone layer above Toronto have brought the global problem of ozone depletion disturbingly close to home. While ozone at ground level is harmful to humans and vegetation, at high levels in the stratosphere it is a shield protecting the earth from harmful ultraviolet radiation. A significant thinning of the ozone layer is expected to lead to a dramatic increase in radiation-induced skin cancers.

Chlorofluorocarbons (CFCs) are the prime culprits implicated in the destruction of the ozone layer. Global recognition of the problem has improved in the past five years, and it appears that the production of CFCs will be largely eliminated by the year 2000. But concerns have already been raised about the chemicals that would replace CFCs: they are considered potent greenhouse gases that will exacerbate global warming.

The foregoing is merely a snapshot of the regional air quality in the Greater Toronto Area. But air quality can also be affected dramatically by local sources: in Toronto's South Riverdale neighbourhood, for example, residents are beset by odours and pollutants from a local lead smelter, a variety of nearby industries, and Metro's Main Sewage Treatment Plant. There are probably similar situations in other areas where industrial and residential land uses conflict.

The Royal Commission's audit of Toronto's Port Industrial Area indicates

that, in areas close to major traffic arteries, levels of dustfall, suspended particulates, and carbon monoxide may affect human health. This may be particularly relevant to the waterfront because of the network of traffic corridors that run from Burlington to Newcastle.

Wildlife

It is difficult to draw an accurate picture of the wildlife that flourished in the Greater Toronto Bioregion before European settlement began in earnest — information is fragmented and comes largely from diaries, articles, and other writings of the time. We do know, however, that the area was rich in animal life: the forests and plains of the Don Valley watershed were alive with beaver, porcupine, timber wolf, black bear, marten, otter, wolverine, lynx, and elk. The extensive coastal marshes and inland wetlands

The real Toronto Bluejay

were host to a variety of ducks, geese, herons, and other birds, as well as reptiles and amphibians. The waters of Lake Ontario and the lower reaches of its rivers teemed with a huge variety of fish including lake trout, herring, sturgeon, salmon, pike, and muskellunge.

The picture today is dramatically different because of loss of wildlife habitat, human predation, and the introduction of persistent chemicals into the environment and foreign species into the bioregion. All these factors have contributed to a significant decrease in wildlife diversity, and wildlife populations which are under stress.

Altering shorelines and filling wetlands has reduced the space available to animals, fish, and birds for living and reproducing. Spawning grounds for cold-water fish have been lost because rivers were dammed.

With the exception of beaver and porcupine, none of the mammals previously found in the Don watershed are now common in the GTA. The passenger pigeon nested in several colonies on the Don watershed and could be found in large numbers in 1870. Clearing of land for farms and intensive market shooting and trapping rendered this handsome bird extinct. The piping plover, with its musical, plaintive voice, used to be resident, in large numbers, in the beaches around the Great Lakes but was declared an endangered species in Ontario in 1977. It no longer nests in the GTA, primarily because of the recreational use of beaches: the destruction of nests and young by people and vehicles and the disturbance of nesting birds.

The numbers of many species of frogs, turtles, and snakes have decreased dramatically in southern Ontario during the 20th century, largely because their habitats have been degraded or destroyed. Many of the reptiles and amphibians inhabiting the remaining coastal marshes in the GTA are classified as rare, including the eastern spiny softshell turtle, as well as the Blanding's, wood, stinkpot, and map turtles.

Fisheries are sensitive to a variety of influences: shoreline alterations, overfishing, pollution, destruction of wetlands, and the introduction of exotic species. Twenty endemic species of fish have disappeared from the Toronto waterfront in the past century, including such valuable sport fish as muskellunge, and species such as herring, which were the backbone of local commercial

Liquid bulk storage, Port Industrial Area

... **Western Europeans and Americans have been carrying around with them as part of their mental baggage a deeply felt and despairing assumption that progress demands degraded surroundings. You put up with such surroundings as long as you have to, and you run away from them as soon as you can afford to, but, this belief has it, deteriorated landscapes and debased communities and bad smells and hideous noises are simply a given — something we all have to live with.**

Hiss, T. 21 August 1989. "Reflections: encountering the countryside: II." *New Yorker* 40.

fishing. While the mouth of the relatively unpolluted Rouge River hosts 31 species of fish, only three can be found in the severely degraded Don.

The bald eagle is rarely found in the Great Lakes Basin, because of chemical contamination there. Originally threatened by habitat loss and hunting, populations began to recover early in the 20th century when protection measures were enacted. However, a rapid decline in populations in the Great Lakes Basin began again in the 1940s, as the result of persistent pesticides such as DDT and dieldrin.

Such chemicals and PCBs were also responsible for the collapse, in the 1970s, of populations of herring gulls, black-crowned night herons, and cormorants in the Toronto area. Prohibition of such chemicals has allowed the herons and gulls to make a recovery, but the cormorant and bald eagle have yet to return to Toronto's shores. This may indicate, in part, how long it takes some of these chemicals to break down completely: although no longer in use, they remain in water, sediments, and tissues. PCBs and mirex, for example, have been banned in Ontario for some time, yet are still found in fish taken from Lake Ontario.

The Ministry of the Environment advises that people restrict their intake of seven species of fish caught in Toronto waters because of high levels of PCBs, mirex, pesticides, mercury, and other metals. Contamination of fish populations occurs all along the Greater Toronto Waterfront, with level and type of contamination varying from location to location.

Levels of contaminants in wildlife are good indicators of ecosystem health. Like the canary in the coal mine, the effects of chemicals in animal populations can be a warning of the potential effects on humans. Persistent organic chemicals and metals can bioaccumulate in animal tissues and levels can increase moving up the food chain. In other words, levels of toxics can be quite low in water, and slightly higher in organisms like zooplankton, but can reach dangerous levels in animals at the top of the chain — such animals as fish-eating birds, turtles, mammals, and even humans.

Humans carry persistent toxics, like the ubiquitous PCBs, in their fatty tissues, especially in the liver and brain, and in breast milk. In wildlife, depending on the chemicals and the species, such contaminants can cause reproductive failures, deformities, and tumours.

Species of wildlife introduced from elsewhere have altered, and in some cases, damaged, the ecosystem. North Americans are only too familiar with the European starling, the house sparrow, and the carp, all imported species that have become nuisances. There are many others in the same category: for example, 11 species of fish along the Toronto waterfront can be classified as introduced, of which the sea lamprey is most notorious — a voracious predator that entered the Great Lakes when the St. Lawrence Seaway was opened. Although largely controlled now, it played a significant role in the decline of certain varieties of sport fish in Lake Ontario.

Today, the tiny zebra mussel is one of the latest immigrants to the Great Lakes; it travelled from Europe in the hold of a ship, entered the water when the bilges were pumped out, and has found our lakes attractive. A prolific breeder, it has been dubbed the "cockroach of the Great Lakes". The mussels are costing millions of dollars in repairs, removal, and lost opportunities. They attach themselves to working and recreational boats, and block water intake pipes, thus frustrating public works departments and industrial users of water.

The tiny molluscs also cover fish-spawning habitat, and consume vast quantities of plankton that are a vital part of the food web for many other species.

For all the reasons outlined — loss of habitat, predation, persistent chemical contaminants, and introduced species — wildlife is under siege in the Greater Toronto Bioregion.

But there is some encouraging news: many river valleys and other green spaces in the region — while not pristine — still provide habitat for wildlife and important links for migration and movement. This is why flying squirrels and deer can still be found in Scarborough's Rouge Valley, or red fox sighted on the Leslie Street Spit.

The Toronto area lies in the overlapping zones of the two major North American migratory flyways, the Atlantic and the Mississippi. The waterfront and its remaining green spaces provide important staging grounds for birds during their spring and fall migrations, allowing stopovers before birds continue south to wintering grounds or north to summer breeding grounds. All too often, however, these green corridors are becoming fragmented by development.

Much of the wildlife habitat that remains is degraded from nearby urban use; protecting and enhancing remaining wildlife will require changes in attitude and adherence to the ecosystem approach, in order to ensure healthy, self-sustaining populations.

Conclusions

This sketch of the air, land, water, wildlife, and human activities in the Greater Toronto Bioregion reveals an ecosystem under considerable stress. Rivers, creeks, and the lake are polluted and unfit for swimming, and cannot be used for drinking water unless they are treated. Persistent organic chemicals and heavy metals are found in the air, water, wildlife, and soils of the region. The pressures of development continue to pose a threat to wildlife habitat and species diversity. Landfills are nearing capacity and more sewage and stormwater run-off is generated than can be effectively treated. Transportation networks are at, or above, capacity. Prime agricultural land and green space are being lost to apparently relentless urbanization, and the Oak Ridges Moraine, a precious resource for groundwater, wildlife,

and open space, is threatened by development pressures.

This is an ecosystem that, to a large degree, is literally "dis-integrated", one in which the carrying capacity — the ability of air, land, and water to absorb the impact of human use — is clearly strained, and cannot be sustained over the long term unless fundamental changes are made.

Who is responsible for tackling these problems? The answer is complicated: governance in the Greater Toronto Bioregion is shared by five regional municipalities, 30 local municipalities, and numerous federal and provincial ministries, departments, boards, agencies, and commissions. In an era when it is clear that governments alone cannot solve our environmental problems, the 6,000 industries in the GTA and its four million residents also have a role to play.

Toronto skyline from Polson Quay, Port of Toronto

The ecosystem approach highlights the interactions among ecological, social, economic, and political systems within the bioregion. It suggests that economic development patterns, resource policies, consumer trends, and public attitudes must all be considered in terms of their actual or potential effect on the integrity of the system. This requires a strong emphasis on setting goals in common, changing attitudes, co-ordinating plans and actions across jurisdictions, co-ordinating mechanisms for allocating and using resources, and planning co-operatively.

Environmental processes are not confined within political boundaries, and actions in one jurisdiction may affect environmental health in others. It is therefore imperative to develop administrative mechanisms that bring jurisdictions together to solve problems co-operatively and to develop environmentally sound ways of living in this bioregion. For example, the Lower Don Task Force in the City of Toronto realizes that any efforts to clean up the Lower Don will be futile unless they are accompanied by co-ordinated action on the part of the two regions and seven municipalities in the watershed.

There is an urgent need for regeneration of the entire Greater Toronto Bioregion to remediate environmental problems caused by past activities, to prevent further degradation, and to ensure that all future activities result in a net improvement in environmental health. In a region experiencing dramatic economic growth and rapid urbanization, it is crucial to heed the warning signs of ecosystem stress, so that the quality of life that attracted people here can be restored and maintained, for existing and future generations.

Focusing on the needs of the Greater Toronto Waterfront in the context of its bioregion, the next chapter offers a set of principles for planning, developing, and managing a healthy, integrated waterfront. Chapter 3 contains specific recommendations for regeneration, both on a waterfront-wide scale and on a local basis.

The Artist's Choice, Don River near Toronto, early 1900s, Edwardian postcard

The Trillium, Ontario's symbol

CHAPTER TWO

PRINCIPLES

Principles

The following principles flow directly from the ecosystem approach to managing the waterfront. They should form the basis of policies and planning for the waterfront by governments at all levels, and should provide a standard against which waterfront development and management, whether public or private, can be evaluated.

In future, policies and proposals along the waterfront should not be judged solely on their economic merits, or their contribution to recreational, housing or other objectives. They must also be judged on whether they contribute to rehabilitating ecological health and public use and enjoyment of the waterfront, or simply continue the pattern of past abuses. Applying these principles forms the foundation for making such a judgement.

Principles for a green waterfront can be expressed simply. It is the view of this Commission that the waterfront should be:

~ **clean;**
~ **green;**
~ **useable;**
~ **diverse;**
~ **open;**
~ **accessible;**
~ **connected;**
~ **affordable;**
~ **attractive.**

The following sections provide a more detailed explanation of the interpretation, origins, and possible applications of these principles.

Clean

~ The air, land, sediments, and water should be free of contaminants that impair beneficial uses by people and other living beings.
~ Water quality should be such that it allows fish to be eaten without restrictions caused by the presence of contaminants; that people can swim and engage in water sports without risk of illness; that levels of potentially toxic chemicals in drinking water remain below detectable limits or meet all accepted health standards.

If the waterfront is to achieve its full potential as an attractive, positive element in the Greater Toronto Bioregion, substantial improvements in present levels of water quality are essential. The magnitude and extent of the problems have been defined by a number of studies, and summarized for the Metro Toronto waterfront in the Commission's Publication No. 10, *East Bayfront and Port Industrial Area: Environment in Transition*, which noted that:

> Although the severity of problems varies, the same ones occur across the waterfront... Bacterial loading causes beaches to be posted. Eutrophication is a continuing problem due to nutrient loadings. Metals and organic chemicals can be found in the water column. Bottom sediments are contaminated with organic chemicals and metals, especially in slips and embayments where water circulation is poor. Aquatic biota bio-accumulate organic chemicals and metals. Good fish habitat is scarce.

The revised Great Lakes Water Quality Agreement defines a list of undesirable changes under its "impairment of beneficial use(s)" clause. These include:

> ... changes in the chemical, physical or biological integrity of the Great Lakes System sufficient to cause any of the following:
>
> i) restrictions on fish and wildlife consumption;
> ii) tainting of fish and wildlife flavour;
> iii) degradation of fish and wildlife populations;

iv) fish tumours or other deformities;

v) bird or animal deformities or reproduction problems;

vi) degradation of benthos;

vii) restrictions on dredging activities;

viii) eutrophication or undesirable algae;

ix) restrictions on drinking water consumption, or taste and odour problems;

x) beach closings;

xi) degradation of aesthetics;

xii) added costs to agriculture or industry;

xiii) degradation of phytoplankton and zooplankton populations; and

xiv) loss of fish and wildlife habitat.

It is evident that the Metro Toronto waterfront now suffers many of those impairments, with the rest of the GTA waterfront affected to a lesser extent.

Correcting this situation will require commitment and co-operative action from many agencies, both along the waterfront and throughout the bioregion. The Metro Toronto Remedial Action Plan process is currently working towards a consensus on the actions necessary, and on the role of various agencies. Other studies, and other committees at various levels, are looking at specific components of environmental restoration.

While much of this discussion is commendable and necessary, it must not become an excuse for inaction. During the Royal Commission's hearings on a Green Strategy

Rouge River — polluted storm sewer run-off

for the Greater Toronto Waterfront, Luciano Martin of Etobicoke described his frustration at the slow implementation of the Toronto Area Watershed Management Strategy, which was completed in 1986:

> On plans that have been approved, I think they should be implemented, and they should be implemented now rather than wait for further studies to restate basically the same problems and come up with what can only be rather similar cures.

Applying the principle that the waterfront should be clean also means that redevelopment or new developments, whether public or private, should assist in resolving problems created in the past. Because a significant component of waterfront pollution comes through tributary streams, it means that developments anywhere in the watershed can no longer be permitted to exacerbate problems — for example, through inadequate control of stormwater or eroded sediments.

In the course of its hearings, the Commission was given a number of suggestions for making improvements to the cleanliness of the waterfront: one deputant proposed a goal of no net increase in the flow of sanitary sewer water into the lake. To meet this goal developers would have to retrofit existing buildings to achieve substantial reductions in water use before they would be allowed to construct new buildings. The same principle has been suggested for stormwater, using design features to direct run-off back into the ground.

Karey Shinn of the Kew Beach Residents Association reminded the Commission of the facilities, either present or planned, that cause air pollution in the Port Industrial Area, including proposed expansions to sludge burning at the Ashbridge's Bay Sewage Treatment Plant, and restarting of the retrofitted R. L. Hearn electrical generating plant. In Ms Shinn's words, "It is fundamentally wrong to ignore the cumulative effects of these actual projects and future projects on our airshed".

Green

~ The diversity and productivity of ecological communities should be protected and restored through measures to:
 ~ preserve the genetic diversity of indigenous plants and animals;
 ~ restore healthy natural habitats and communities;
 ~ maintain natural ecological processes.
~ Natural vegetation should be used to restore and enhance the attractiveness, health, and usability of human communities.

Sport fishing in Lake Ontario

A rich variety of species is the cornerstone of a healthy ecosystem, with all species having a role to play. The trend in recent years has been a gradual but inexorable impoverishment of wild species along the waterfront. Today, such wildlife as common and black terns, spiny softshell and wood turtles, and redbelly and milk snakes are threatened. One hundred and forty kinds of

Swans in the Pumphouse Marsh, Oshawa

plants are known to occur at only one site in the GTA, while 109 species of plants and wildlife occurring within the GTA are classed as provincially rare. Given that genetic diversity is a minimum standard for a healthy ecosystem, this alarming decline must be reversed.

In its natural state, the waterfront is one of the most diverse and productive ecosystems in the temperate climatic zone. However, the productivity of the GTA ecosystem has been impaired, primarily by destruction and interference with natural habitats, but also by degraded water quality, and noise. Natural communities are resilient and many species of fish, wildlife, and plants will return if appropriate habitats are provided. The "miracle" of the spectacular wildlife populations now found on the Leslie Street Spit demonstrates how quickly natural communities respond when favourable conditions are restored.

In part, the principle of a green waterfront reinforces the need to preserve those areas of natural habitat remaining along the shore. However, it also requires an unprecedented effort to recreate habitats destroyed by past abuses. Habitat creation measures should include:

~ making naturalization an essential element in park planning;
~ creating wetlands and offshore islands for wildlife use;
~ replacing rocky shoals and other fish habitats;
~ restoring vegetation along rivers and streams.

Management of natural areas along the waterfront should not employ the single-species approach that now characterizes most wildlife planning, but should, instead, emphasize the need to protect rare species, restore wildlife communities, and enhance species diversity.

This change in emphasis has already taken place in fisheries management. The Ministry of Natural Resources, through its Strategic Plan for Ontario Fisheries II, has adopted a goal of creating healthy, sustainable aquatic ecosystems that are based on maintaining and restoring naturally reproducing populations of native species.

Naturalists' and sportspersons' associations, as well as members of the public, can be involved in restoring the health of ecological systems. Projects such as the tree-planting days sponsored by the Lower Don Task Force or the stream rehabilitation projects of the Black Creek group (a citizen's group active on this branch of the Humber River system) are among current examples of useful public involvement.

Wildlife agencies, school boards, businesses or municipalities could sponsor contests on ways to create habitat, and then provide financial and technical support for the best suggestions. Developers could be encouraged to make habitat enhancement a part of their plans.

To measure the effectiveness of greening the waterfront, key species should be identified as indicators of the state of our ecosystem and should be monitored periodically to evaluate changes in diversity and population levels.

As Marion Strebig of the Federation of Ontario Naturalists pointed out at a Commission hearing, indicator species should be chosen for the role they play in the ecosystem, rather than for their attractiveness to human beings:

> Why not take as an indicator species a humble thing like the Caddisfly, which acts as a basic food source for many species in the aquatic system? [Its] disappearance is a sure indication of trouble.

Over the past decade, volunteer atlas projects have added greatly to our knowledge of the numbers and distribution of birds and herptiles (reptiles and amphibians) in the ecosystem, and discussions are under way on a provincial mammal atlas. The data for this atlas could form the basis of more detailed

For many residents in the Basin, Areas of Concern are remembered as pristine natural areas that once harboured secret swimming holes, spawning grounds for fish and sanctuary for birds and other wildlife. Urban, agricultural and industrial development destroyed wetlands and other vital habitat. It is estimated that two thirds of the wetlands in the Great Lakes Basin have been destroyed.

1990. "Habitat restoration." In *RAP revival: a citizens' agenda for RAPS: report from A Remedial Action Plan Workshop for Citizen Leaders, February 9-11, 1990, Stella Niagara, New York,* 14. Buffalo: Great Lakes United.

information collection and monitoring along the waterfront, using the abilities and enthusiasm of local naturalists.

The control of populations of such species as giant Canada geese is also related to promoting ecological diversity. When they reach nuisance levels, wild species are themselves a symptom of an ecosystem under stress, in which normal checks and balances have failed. In addition to the very real conflict between geese and recreational users of the waterfront, their abundance interferes with the potential for other species. A control strategy that combines habitat modification and population control by federal and provincial wildlife agencies would be appropriate.

The locations of most significant habitats and natural areas along the GTA waterfront are known; a good many are already in public ownership. However, a substantial number of critical habitats remain unprotected,

and it is vital that their future be secured. Among the most important sites in need of additional protection, through either public ownership or other means, are:

~ Joshua Creek mouth (Mississauga);
~ Frenchman's Bay marshes (Pickering);
~ Carruther's Creek mouth (Ajax);
~ Lynde Creek mouth (Whitby);
~ Pumphouse Marsh (Oshawa) ;
~ Second Marsh (Oshawa);
~ McLaughlin Bay (Newcastle);
~ West Side Beach Marsh (Newcastle);
~ Wilmot Creek (Newcastle);
~ Bond Head Bluffs (Newcastle).

As well, as noted in the Commission's Publication No. 8, *A Green Strategy for the Greater Toronto Waterfront*, natural creek mouths and other areas of local significance should be protected wherever possible. These

The G'mas Maple

Port of Toronto eastern end of Ship Channel

Ontario is still undergoing rapid development. Constant land use pressure on an area whose size remains constant assures the continual loss of field, forest and marsh which make up the rich tapestry of the landscape. We cannot turn back the clock, but we can rescue some pieces of green from the diminishing legacy.

Hilts, S. G. 1986. "Why protect natural heritage?" In *Islands of green: natural heritage protection in Ontario*, 24. Toronto: Ontario Heritage Foundation.

include the mouth of Fourteen Mile and Shoreacres creeks in Halton, and Graham and Port Granby creeks in Durham.

The Commission is aware that plans to secure some of these priority sites are under way, and encourages all such efforts. For example, we hope that the present unsatisfactory state of Pumphouse Marsh can be corrected, in response to pressure from the South Oshawa Residents Association, combined with the stated willingness of the City of Oshawa to assume management of the marsh.

Evidence from deputants at the Commission's hearings cited praiseworthy examples of co-operation to protect natural habitats: Hugh Peacock of the Durham Region Field Naturalists noted General Motors' exemplary treatment of stormwater and other environmental concerns during design and construction of its headquarters, adjacent to Oshawa's Second Marsh. This contrasts greatly, he pointed out, to environmentally destructive practices carried out behind the Atlantic Packaging plant on Corbett Creek, as well as along many other areas of the waterfront.

As the experience at Rattray Marsh in Mississauga has shown, development that does not provide sufficient buffer for wetland or treat stormwater adequately can greatly reduce the value of the habitat. This points out the complexity of protecting ecological communities in an urban setting, which involves more than simply setting aside the habitat as green space. Such issues could be better dealt with if official plans for municipalities and watershed plans by conservation authorities incorporated special species conservation objectives and if municipalities created ecological advisory committees such as the one now operating in the Halton Region.

processes be understood and addressed before shore protection or lakefill projects are approved in other waterfront areas.

The migration of birds and butterflies is another natural process. Because many species need to build up their energy reserves before crossing the expanse of Lake Ontario, it is essential to protect lakeside resting and feeding habitats, as well as green corridors through urban areas.

Elements of the natural ecosystem, especially trees and shrubs, are vital to both people and wildlife. John Macintyre of the Parks

Rail passenger access to downtown Toronto

Several examples of natural ecological processes can be found along the waterfront. Natural patterns of sand scour and deposition along the shore nourish beaches; when the continuing natural erosion of the Scarborough Bluffs required substantial control measures, the resulting decline in transported sand created a new problem by "starving" the Eastern Beaches. Such processes, once altered, can be very difficult to correct. It is important that the potential impact on sand transport

and Recreation Federation of Ontario reminded the Commission of the critical role of trees in a green legacy:

> Trees are important to our physical environment and to our emotional well being. They remove pollutants from the air, reduce noise and have a moderating effect on the climate — essentially acting as nature's air-conditioners.

58

Useable

~ The waterfront should continue to support a mix of public and private uses that:
  ~ are primarily water-related;
  ~ permit public access, use, and enjoyment of the water's edge;
  ~ enhance residential neighbourhoods and appropriate industrial uses;
  ~ are environmentally friendly in form and function;
  ~ minimize conflicts with adjacent communities or uses;
  ~ promote greater year-round use.

An attractive and vibrant waterfront supports a wide range of uses beyond recreation areas and green spaces: residential neighbourhoods, industry and commerce, utilities, and transportation facilities all have places there. As one deputant stated in his submission:

It is possible, through good planning practices and policies, to develop an environmentally friendly waterfront which does not preclude a mix of land uses. What is required if this is to be accomplished are comprehensive environmental management and development control policies as well as parks and open space policies.

Urban waterfronts were once largely industrial. Ports dominated waterfronts and became the focus of commercial activity based on the movement by ship of raw materials and finished goods. The growth and economic well-being of the ports' hinterland were directly linked to the successful operation of the port terminals. The federal government established public ports in the Greater Toronto Area at Toronto and Oshawa. In addition, there are several private port facilities to serve specific industries (such as cement manufacturing and oil refineries); their ongoing role on the waterfront is linked to the future of those industries.

In both Toronto and Oshawa, the dominant position of the public industrial ports has been eroded by changing technologies and shipping patterns, lack of growth opportunities, competition from other ports and from surface transportation, and lessened need for marine transportation to meet consumer demands.

The Port of Toronto currently serves as a transfer, storage, and distribution centre for bulk commodities such as cement, sugar, aggregates, and soybeans. It also handles liquid bulk commodities and a range of general cargo. The demand for the functions it carries out is expected to continue to make it an active part of the Toronto waterfront.

Woe to you who add house to house and join field to field, till no space is left and you live alone in the land.

1978. "Isaiah 5:8." In *The holy bible: new international version*, 737. Grand Rapids: Zondervan.

The Port of Oshawa serves specific local industries, but plays a small role in the overall context of transportation and industrial requirements of the region. Over the past decade, the tonnages being handled have declined, with such commodities as coal and salt now moving through the private port facilities at St. Mary's Cement. While the Port of Oshawa has been successful in attracting some new traffic, there is great pressure to develop alternate uses for the port lands.

While the manufacturing and port uses of the waterfront have diminished somewhat, industry continues to be a valuable and legitimate part of the waterfront mix of uses. In keeping with the principles of this report, waterfront industry should be non-polluting and, where possible, should contribute to appropriate public uses of the waterfront. Special emphasis should be placed on policies

The mouth of the Rouge River

that will lead to the development of green-enterprise industries for the next century.

As the industrial use of the waterfront declines, a large number of sites are undergoing redevelopment, generally involving more intense use and often based on a change to residential use.

The nature of these changes is well illustrated by the conversion now under way at industrial sites in Etobicoke, Mississauga, and the Port Union area of Scarborough. This redevelopment process opens opportunities to secure greater public access to the shore, to bring strategic parcels of land into public hands, and, using creative landscaping and design, to create a more attractive and inviting waterfront. It may also provide opportunities for rehabilitation of contaminated environments at former industrial sites.

However, in order to achieve these benefits, waterfront projects must be evaluated carefully. Protecting the waterfront environment and creating public access and links must be an integral part of project planning. Given the limited extent of the waterfront, it must be clearly demonstrated that projects will enhance the environment and make the waterfront more publicly accessible.

Residential neighbourhoods are a long-standing and legitimate use of parts of the waterfront. Stable neighbourhoods should be protected and linked through a trail system to form a chain of neighbourhoods along the lake. The principles outlined in this chapter should be applied in planning for any redevelopment that occurs or as new residential areas are developed.

Because the waterfront is a limited environment being asked to meet increased and competing demands, one criterion for assessing proposed uses should be their relationship to the water: those that require water access should take preference although other general uses may sometimes need to be

The mouth of the Don River

We have a funny complex in North America about nature. We don't understand the real rapport between man and his surroundings. We've had a fear of nature and yet we say we love it — and a fear of ourselves in relationship to nature. This has led to two reactions. Either we want to go into the wilderness where nobody has been; or we want to destroy it completely. In North America you seldom find the extraordinary magic that exists when what man has done complements or makes more beautiful what nature has prepared. We have to re-establish that rapport.

Erickson, A. 4 October 1980. In *In Erickson's Eden, an architect can improve on nature*, A. Freedman. E3. *Globe and Mail*.

accommodated near the shore. The same should apply to waterfront recreational uses: preference should be given to those that have to be on the water's edge — whether that involves marinas or boat ramps or simply the opportunity for quiet walks along the shore.

Because the growing GTA population will require additional or expanded services in the coming years, one facet of waterfront use that deserves special attention relates to public utilities, including generating stations, waste management facilities, and water and sewage works. While utility lands and works can be barriers to sections of the shore, they also constitute substantial parcels of public land that could be devoted to more than a single use. The design of all new or upgraded works should incorporate provisions for public access along the shore, through setbacks of facilities or other design features. Existing parcels should be reviewed to identify opportunities for trail crossings or other public uses.

The locations of new works should also be scrutinized carefully to ensure that they conflict as little as possible with natural features, existing residential neighbourhoods or recreational uses. As is evident in the current plans for expanding the regional water plant on the Ajax waterfront, there is often a tendency to view passive open space as the least costly place to locate facilities. The proposed plant in Ajax will mean a major loss of existing green space, and will create a visual barrier to the waterfront. Creative landscaping and building design should

Among the suggested projects are promotion of environmentally friendly industry; state-of-the-art waste management systems in residential, commercial, and industrial communities; conservation strategies for energy and water consumption; and innovative, environmentally sound planning and transportation initiatives.

While all of these might be part of any urban location, it is particularly appropriate to consider them in a waterfront setting, where environmental concerns are highlighted.

Covered salt pile, Port Industrial Area

address these problems with a view to integrating the structure with the surrounding residential neighbourhood.

The waterfront can also be ideal as the location of urban uses and practices that are more friendly to the environment. The Metro Toronto Waterfront Committee has suggested a new form of provincial-municipal partnership that would sponsor a series of demonstration projects aimed at producing an environmentally friendly waterfront.

At present, many recreational activities and some jobs along the waterfront are seasonally based. In her submission to the Commission, planning consultant Xenia Klinger suggested that paying greater attention to microclimatic effects when designing a building, as well as carefully planned planting of evergreens, could increase the comfort levels and the use of waterfront settings beyond the traditional summer season.

According to a 1989 Environment Canada study, reducing wind chill by improving design and tree-planting could add 56 days of year-round park use, an increase of about 50 per cent.

In its submission to the Royal Commission, the Board of Trade of Metropolitan Toronto also urged greater attention to off-season use; it proposed a study on winter use of the waterfront, in order to make more use of existing facilities and lands.

Diverse

~ Waterfront uses, programs, and environments should provide diverse experiences for visitors and residents.
~ The mix of open space and recreation facilities should balance competing public demands within environmental limits.
~ Waterfront uses should be balanced between:
  ~ public and private;
  ~ urban and rural;
  ~ the built and natural environments;
  ~ large- and small-scale;
  ~ active and passive;
  ~ busy and quiet;
  ~ free and user-pay.

One of the recurring themes in discussions about the waterfront is the concept of diversity. One way to enhance diversity along the waterfront is to develop a linked system of parklands and recreation facilities. Bob Short of the Town of Whitby was among the deputants who endorsed the idea of a system of green spaces, noting that waterfront plans could:

include a hierarchy of open space functions and differentiate between locally significant open space resources, and those areas that ... provide larger opportunities for the growing populations within the GTA.

Jane Welsh of the City of Mississauga told the Commission that:

successful waterfronts tend to be places where opportunity exists for

diverse experiences. There should be opportunities for solitude, places for crowds, quiet boardwalks, and busy promenades.

To tap the potential attractiveness of the waterfront most fully, diversity must be within easy reach of members of any individual waterfront community as well as across the entire waterfront. It must relate not only to patterns of land use but also to the diversity of experiences and settings in both the built and natural environments.

The expectation that a Port will inevitably handle all the cargo to and from its 'naturally tributary hinterland' has been shattered by the load center port — the single destination to or from which containers can easily be transported overland, trucked, or carried by rail to an entire region. Many Ports are now bypassed by cargoes that they once would have handled as a kind of geographical right.

Chasan, D. J. and T. J. Dowd. 1988. "Strategic planning: defining port values." In *Urban ports and harbor management: responding to change along U.S. waterfronts*, editor M. J. Hershman. 238. New York: Taylor & Francis.

Natural shoreline, Frenchman's Bay

As part of its proposed waterfront plan, the City of Mississauga has put forward six categories of waterfront green space:

~ Windows to the Lake: small areas of public land such as street ends, that provide local visual access and passive uses.

~ Local Access Nodes: providing lake access to neighbourhoods with foot or bicycle access, as well as minimal facilities as stopover or rest areas for pedestrians and cyclists touring the waterfront.

~ Regional Access Nodes: gathering places and dispersion points for people from local communities and beyond, on a larger landbase.

~ Natural Areas: places of minimal development managed to preserve and enhance their natural appearance and condition.

~ Activity Centres: containing specific attractions such as marinas, commercial outlets, and facilities for structured recreation, large events, and places where people can congregate.

~ Linkages: designed to provide connections between green spaces, and between those spaces and adjacent communities.

Similar green-space classification systems should be employed as part of the planning process across the waterfront. Taken together, such spaces would create a green fabric of varying widths and textures over the entire length of the waterfront.

Underlying much of the comment at the hearings was the assumption that future recreational use of the waterfront is likely to be much greater than in the past, thanks to a variety of factors. These include: expected population growth in the Greater Toronto Area; improvements to the quality and accessibility of the waterfront; growing public interest in the environment; and changing attitudes towards recreation and lifestyle choices. In time, this increasing demand is expected to lead to stiffer competition for scarce and limited land on the waterfront, and to more intense uses of land adjacent to the water's edge.

Given that context, it is essential to recognize that not all uses can be accommodated at all sites. Waterfront planning must pay special attention to protecting natural areas and passive open space along the water, pieces of green that are an essential part of the urban infrastructure — as necessary to the fabric of the community as its roads and sewers. As the size and complexity of the urban area expands, the value of these open areas rises correspondingly.

Without a strong commitment to preserving waterfront green space as an essential part of the broader system, that space is inevitably nibbled away for other, more active uses. The Commission has already commented on the proposed location of the aquarium in Humber Bay Park East, which is just one case in point.

The Commission believes that, while it will always be difficult to strike a balance among uses along the waterfront, the two most vital considerations are public demand and environmental limits. Demand is influenced by the fact that we are an aging population, living in a larger and denser fabric of communities, for whom passive and natural waterfront spaces are increasingly more valuable.

In speaking of environmental limits, the Commission has in mind the cumulative effects of recreational activities and facilities on the natural ecosystem along the waterfront, as well as such public concerns as traffic congestion and crowding.

Open

~ The density and design of waterfront structures should not create a visual barrier or be an intrusion on the water's edge.
~ The water's edge should be, and clearly be identified as, open to public access.

The most frequent criticism of proposed central waterfront development was the scale and density of high-rise development, which was seen as creating a wall of concrete between the city and the water. Although proposals for that area of the Central Waterfront devoted to Harbourfront have been scaled back, they have become a potent symbol of what people do not want their waterfront to be.

Human life, to be fully human, needs the city, but it also needs food and other raw materials gained from the country. Everybody needs ready access to both countryside and city. It follows that the aim must be a *pattern* of urbanization so that every rural area has a nearby city, near enough so that people can visit it and be back the same day. No other pattern makes human sense.

Schumacher, F. 1985. In *Dwellers in the land: the bioregional vision*, K. Sale. 114. San Francisco: Sierra Club.

In fact, Harbourfront has become a kind of shorthand — referring to future development in Etobicoke and elsewhere along the waterfront, people told the Commission strongly: "We don't want another Harbourfront here."

What people do want, it appears, is a waterfront that has a feeling of openness and spaciousness, and that allows visitors to escape from the confines of the urban form. Most deputants welcomed diversity of amenities and attractions, both summer and winter, as making time spent at the waterfront more interesting. However, they also want ample

Oakville's Gairloch Gardens

open space and vistas, even in places where the city touches the waterfront. Implicit in this desire for an open waterfront is the desire to create and protect views to the water from adjacent streets or activity areas.

In a few cases, waterfront lands that are actually public have, in effect, been privatized by design features that obscure access or make the public feel unwelcome. For example, many people are not aware that the land at the foot of Bay Street, which has the look and feel of a private space for residents only, is actually public land and free for their use. The design of public lands on the water near large urban redevelopment projects, such as the Etobicoke Motel Strip, must be carefully reviewed to ensure that they are visible and welcoming.

Being able to walk along the water's edge is one measure of how open the waterfront feels. The City of Toronto and the Town of Oakville are among municipalities that have established policies and programs to bring the water's edge into public ownership. Their programs are commendable and should be explored by other municipalities. However, it should be remembered that the goal is public access, not necessarily public ownership — for example, in situations where easements or access agreements for private or institutional lands can provide appropriate access at much lower costs. Whatever the methods, redevelopment activities along the waterfront should provide all possible opportunities for people to gain public access along the water's edge.

Accessible

~ All waterfront activity nodes and communities should be accessible by public transit as well as by road, with increasing emphasis on transit.

~ The waterfront should be easily accessible by foot or bicycle, with major

Summer sailboarding on Kelso Lake, Kelso Conservation Area, Milton

improvements where necessary to overcome the barriers presented by road and rail corridors.

~ The waterfront should be safe, and accessible to the disabled as well as all other sectors of society.

~ Transportation planning in the waterfront area should:

    ~ take into account the impact of automotive traffic on the environment;

    ~ establish an appropriate balance among rapid transit, surface transit, road transportation, and passenger rail;

    ~ relate waterfront, environmental, and land-use objectives to transportation capacity priorities;

    ~ strengthen commuter, freight, and inter-city rail and air services, as appropriate;

~ explore such innovative facilities as waterborne passenger transportation.

Green space along the Greater Toronto Waterfront takes its form within an essentially urban context; as Bill McLean of the Metropolitan Toronto and Region Conservation Authority pointed out to the Commission, the concept of green space itself is essentially an urban one.

Within this context, and from a broader environmental perspective, developing attractions for large numbers of people without providing effective public transit would be short-sighted at best. Public transit to waterfront sites not only relieves the pollution and congestion associated with vehicle traffic, it also makes the waterfront more accessible to people of all incomes and reduces the amount of open space used for parking lots.

One of the key elements of accessibility to the waterfront is the way in which smaller parcels of waterfront green space are integrated into the community. Areas within reach of foot and bicycle traffic reduce the need for car travel and parking. Some communities, including Toronto, Oshawa, and Ajax, have made considerable progress in linking waterfront parks to the community, using valley trails, formal walkways, and related green spaces; others should consider such links.

Integration is sometimes more difficult. For example, Toronto's Parkdale community is effectively cut off from the waterfront by expressway and train corridors. One potential solution is construction of a Parkdale

**I'm truly sorry man's dominion
has broken nature's social union
an' justifies that ill opinion,
which makes thee startle
at me, thy poor, earth-born
companion,
an' *fellow mortal!***

Burns, R. 1969. "To a Mouse, on Turning Her Up in Her Nest, with a Plough, November 1785", In *Burns' poems and songs*, J. Kingsley. London: Oxford University Press.

The Martin Goodman Trail, Cherry Beach

Deck, which would extend the urban area across these barriers towards the water. In much of Scarborough, access to the water's edge is restricted by the steep bluffs there. Ongoing erosion control work by MTRCA, coupled with development of stairways in some locations, should gradually improve access.

Concerns about the accessibility of the waterfront are particularly crucial for children, the elderly, and the physically chal-

lenged. In recent years, some Harbourfront programs have made real attempts to reach out to these groups, but much more could be done.

Accessibility to the waterfront is reduced for women by concerns about their physical safety. For example, the desolate, confusing pedestrian approaches created by the railway underpasses and the Gardiner/Lake Shore

York Street access to the Waterfront

Corridor are obstacles in the Central Waterfront.

Any future study on improved facilities should incorporate the need to ensure that the waterfront is physically and psychologically accessible to all groups, not just to some. Fear for personal safety must not be allowed to become a barrier to full use and enjoyment of the waterfront. Safety is enhanced when facilities are well used, well lit, and clearly visible. Attractive designs, a rich palette of textures and colours, inviting fragrances and sounds can do a great deal to make the waterfront attractive to everyone.

Many sections of the waterfront have the regional roads and railways necessary to move people and goods between communities. In some cases, the routes are linked

Natural shoreline in Darlington Provincial Park, Newcastle

to waterfront industry or activity centres, but most transportation facilities simply pass through the waterfront area, with little relation to land uses there.

In the past, the development of these facilities has been based almost solely on transportation needs, with little consideration of their effects on the waterfront, the quality of the environment or surrounding land uses. The results in the Central Waterfront have been detrimental and long-lasting, with access to the lake severely constrained by a broad swath of railway lines and the Lake Shore/Gardiner Corridor.

The ecosystem approach to waterfront transportation issues means recognizing the way various aspects affect each other — traffic congestion, the balance of transportation types, the need to renew the existing system, the quality of the waterfront environment, access to the waterfront, and major land-use decisions in the surrounding area. Therefore, decisions on the future of Toronto's transportation system cannot be made on the basis of projected vehicle counts and road capacities alone — they must be based on broader considerations.

At the same time, firm decisions on the future of key transportation facilities — most notably the Lake Shore/Gardiner Corridor — are vital to a host of other planning issues. All along the Gardiner Expressway, from Exhibition Place in the west through Harbourfront and the Railway Lands in the core to Ataratiri and the proposed St. Lawrence Park development in the east, there are major redevelopment proposals that would be affected, even reshaped, by a decision on the Gardiner. In this context, procrastination could mean higher costs and fewer opportunities in future to create a green and healthy city.

There have been suggestions that the Greater Toronto Area could take advantage of its waterfront to provide waterborne passenger services along the Lake Ontario shore. While the feasibility of this concept is uncertain, it is an additional form of public transit, the development of which should be encouraged where appropriate.

Connected

~ The waterfront should be linked by continuous pedestrian and bicycle trails from Burlington to Newcastle.

~ Major green corridors should connect the waterfront, valley systems, and the Oak Ridges Moraine.

~ Waterfront planning should emphasize connections to the waterfront's natural and cultural heritage.

The concept of a continuous Waterfront Trail has been put forward as part of MTRCA's Greenspace Plan, and is incorporated in several municipal waterfront plans. However, there is currently no mechanism for co-ordination, to ensure, for example, that muni-

cipal trails connect at the boundaries or that all municipalities embrace the concept of a continuous trail.

A waterfront trail does not always have to be located right along the water's edge, although that should usually be the first choice. A trail could occasionally leave the shore where it was necessary to bypass obstacles or where it was possible to incorporate such features of interest as historic neighbourhoods. In places, the trail might follow quiet residential streets. However, every effort should be made to separate the waterfront trail from busy arterial roads.

The pedestrian and cycling components of the trail should be separate. Where that is not possible, special efforts should be made to create safe and complementary shared trails.

To be successful, a Waterfront Trail must have considerable public support and involvement. A Waterfront Trail membership association could become a driving force in advocating and planning the trail, and could play an important role in its development, maintenance, and promotion. Unlike the existing long-distance trails in rural parts of Ontario, however, a Waterfront Trail in a mostly urban landscape would probably not be feasible unless there were direct provincial and municipal involvement.

As noted previously, the health and quality of the waterfront are closely linked to its adjacent watersheds. Yet in some areas, the intrusions of the city have pinched off the natural connections between the lakefront and the hinterland, which most often occur through river valleys. In order to maintain ecological and recreational connections, special attention should be paid to major corridors up the valleys of Grindstone Creek, Bronte Creek, Sixteen Mile Creek, the Credit, the Humber, the Don, the Rouge, Duffin Creek, Lynde Creek, Oshawa Creek, Bowmanville/Soper Creek, and Wilmot Creek. As well, local initiatives to create or maintain natural corridors in other areas should be fully supported.

In most cases, these valleys serve as connectors between the waterfront and the natural habitats associated with the Oak Ridges Moraine. As well, the City of Burlington's presentation to the Commission pointed out that its staff will be developing a "green linkages policy" that will "consider opportunities to link natural features such as the Escarpment to the waterfront".

Ecological and recreational links across the GTA must be considered in two categories:

rivers. Man's greed will not be satisfied until the Duffin runs as black as the Don.

If that future is to be avoided, strategies must be conceived to protect the entire cross-section of the valley from development, and to establish a top-of-bank buffer at key parts of the headwaters. Bill McLean of the MTRCA outlined its efforts to interpret the "conservation of land" section of its

Oakville waterfront promenade

maintenance and restoration. While some streams and valleylands are still of excellent quality, the pressures for development are unrelenting. After praising the cultural and natural values of the Duffin Creek corridor, Jim Wiseman of the Pickering Ajax Citizens Together (PACT) painted a bleak picture of its possible future:

> The herons will be the first to go, then the trees, then the farmlands, then the

regulations more broadly, to include the ecological significance of valleylands. This is in contrast to the present practice of considering only erosion problems which, in many cases, can be "engineered" to allow development to proceed on valley slopes, thereby interrupting the integrity of the green corridor. Broadening MTRCA regulations to reflect current ecological values would be an extremely useful step.

Restoration of connecting corridors will require considerable time and public

Toronto Waterfront high-rise development

investment. For instance, the Commission heard from the Don Valley Task Force about the need to recreate a mouth for the Don, to replace the present "urban orifice". In his submission, Dr. Mark Taylor said:

> We should develop a green corridor between Leslie Street Spit, Cherry Beach, and the Don River valley to facilitate the movement of birds and other animals, the foxes, throughout the City. By planting trees and shrubs along the lower Don, we can extend this corridor, cool the water by providing shade, and improve the aesthetics of this transportation corridor.

Connections along the waterfront can go beyond the physical to include links to our heritage. The need to maintain ties to the past was highlighted in the report of the Parks, Pleasures, and Public Amenities Work Group (see the Royal Commission's Publication No. 4). Such ties can be made not only by sensitive adaptation of historic buildings, but also by preserving elements of our marine and industrial heritage and of historical patterns of development.

Heritage connections can also contribute to public education. Dr. John Westgate of the University of Toronto suggested that a Green Strategy provides:

> an opportunity for educational input on our environment through the provision of facilities and programs

Toronto Island Ferry

Bluffer's Park Marina, Scarborough

that would increase awareness of our environment and give a better understanding of our environmental heritage, especially the geology, archaeology, historical and cultural.

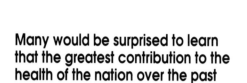

Many would be surprised to learn that the greatest contribution to the health of the nation over the past 150 years was made, not by doctors or hospitals, but by local government.

Parfit, J. 1987. *The health of a city: Oxford, 1770-1974*, Preface. Oxford: Amate Press.

Several educational and interpretive centres have been proposed along the waterfront, including ones at Tommy Thompson Park and Duffin Creek, but none has yet been constructed. Dr. Westgate noted particularly the educational potential at Bluffer's Park and at the Don Valley Brickyards.

Another aspect of public education is the issue of water quality and its restoration. While there is certainly a high degree of awareness that the waterfront is polluted, at least in places, people need a much clearer understanding of the connections between the sources and effects of that pollution, and of the steps needed to restore water quality. As quality improves, the public should also be educated on the progress being made, so that people will continue to support restoration projects and use water resources appropriately. The return of salmon to the Thames River was a powerful symbol of progress against pollution. Our own waterfront needs to develop similar public symbols as measures of progress.

Affordable

~ Waterfront parks and facilities should be financially available to all income groups.
~ Waterfront residential projects should include affordable housing.

The waterfront should belong to everyone; in economic terms, that means there must be a balance of affordable recreation opportunities and a mix of housing types to allow people at all income levels and of all family types the opportunity to live on or near the waterfront. In the words of the Parks, Pleasures, and Public Amenities Work Group's report (Royal Commission Publication No. 4):

> Waterfront communities should not be restricted to only the well-heeled, double income, childless or retired couples so eagerly sought by some condominium developers.

Applying this principle to housing will be difficult, especially as improvements along the waterfront mean that land values escalate even higher. The Commission's Housing and Neighbourhoods Work Group suggested that, in Metro Toronto, affordable housing will have to be developed largely as co-operative and non-profit housing. While the provincial Affordable Housing Policy Statement — which requires that a minimum of 25 per cent of housing in all private development be affordable — will be helpful, the work group suggested that a higher target would be appropriate when public lands are involved. The Commission also notes that many existing neighbourhoods along the waterfront provide higher-than-average components of affordable housing. To retain their affordability, especially as family housing, these stable neighbourhoods must be protected from the escalating land values that accompany redevelopment pressures.

Keeping waterfront recreation affordable is a challenge that can be met, in part, by continuing the general practice of not charging

admission to passive green spaces. Where there is an admission fee to more active facilities and programs, "free days" could be instituted, as is done at such places as the Louvre in Paris. The efforts of Harbourfront to offer affordable programs to families, residents, and tourists are good examples of sensitivity to this principle.

The Commission heard evidence that community-based sailing clubs, such as the member groups of the Outer Harbour Sailing Federation, provide low-cost recreational access for a significant body of users. This approach could be encouraged elsewhere along the waterfront. In addition, the public agencies that act as landlords for these clubs should make every effort to provide secure tenure, and to ensure that rent increases do not jeopardize the affordability of access they provide.

The mix of recreational facilities being provided also greatly affects the affordability of the waterfront. Boat-launch ramps, for

Family fishing, Darlington Provincial Park

example, generally offer more opportunities to lower-income groups than do marina slips. So do waterfront trails, which are free of charge. Even when a trail passes through formal recreation areas, every effort should be made to preserve the concept of its use free of charge.

Attractive

~ Design and landscaping should produce distinctive and memorable places along the waterfront.
~ Waterfront design should:
    ~ protect vistas and views of the lake;
    ~ emphasize sensitive design and massing of buildings;
    ~ consider the relationship between buildings, open spaces, and the water;

~ create desirable microclimates;

~ incorporate attractive and useable links;

~ use harmonious colours, textures, and materials;

~ use natural, as well as manicured, landscape techniques.

Landscape architect Richard Moore urged the Commission to be concerned not just with the quantity of green space along the waterfront, but with its quality:

> We think you have to capture the unique qualities of our heritage, our culture, and our landscape and express them through excellent design to create a series of memorable places... Maybe the waterfront is our embassy and maybe because of that it's got to be designed with distinction, and reflect our special qualities as people that live along the waterfront.

Mr. Moore also suggested that the traditional planning of highly manicured parklands needs to be creatively challenged by innovative plans that embrace the concepts of sustainable development and ecological management, rather than using purely ornamental approaches.

These suggestions were echoed by other deputants, who proposed a "sacred places" policy to preserve areas of outstanding natural or cultural heritage along the waterfront. Developer William Teron, for example, emphasized the potential of a quality waterfront to "uplift the spirit of the entire Metropolitan city and to affect the quality of life and the value of property for all its residents".

Attractive and appropriate design is particularly important along the water's edge. Inevitably, the width of a public access strip along it will vary according to the nature of adjacent land uses and the feasibility of securing adjacent lands. But it should also be influenced by the nature of public activities and uses expected to take place: generally

speaking, the public shoreline strip should be wider in new developments. In places where existing developments dictate a narrower strip, landscaping should be of a quality and intensity that ensure the strip is useful and attractive to the public.

Householders are also users and polluters: it is not just industry, it is not just big government, it is not just corporations. This is where stewardship and accountability come home in a very direct way. This stewardship and accountability is the very basis to anticipate and prevent environmental problems, and it is the only way that we are going to get away from this react and cure type of problem that has proved so expensive....

Gamble, D. 23 May 1990. "Presentation to the Royal Commission on the Future of the Toronto Waterfront public hearings on environment and health, part II." In *Transcript: public hearings on environment and health, part II*, 112. Toronto: Canada. Royal Commission on the Future of the Toronto Waterfront.

Shoreline protection near South Marine Drive, Scarborough

Mimico Housing Co-operative, Etobicoke

One example presented to the Commission was a proposed mixed-use redevelopment on the East Bayfront by the St. Lawrence Park group. This project would provide a well-designed and attractive linear park along the water's edge, and incorporate both public transit and Martin Goodman Trail links in its design.

The Commission is confident that, by adhering to the principles outlined above, and implementing them in all waterfront plans and developments — including in ways suggested in the following chapter — the waterfront can be restored to ecological health to serve the diverse needs of this and future generations.

CHAPTER THREE

REGENERATION

Regeneration

A. AREA-WIDE ISSUES

Regenerating the Toronto waterfront and the watershed of which it is a part depends on taking actions that affect both the entire area and specific localities within it. The first section of this chapter describes recommendations applicable to the waterfront and watershed, while the second discusses those prescribed for defined areas.

1. Implementing an Ecosystem Approach

As outlined in the first two chapters of this report, successful efforts to restore the health and usefulness of the waterfront will depend, in large measure, on an ecosystem approach. By its nature, such an approach cannot be implemented by any one agency or government in isolation. Rather, a wide range of agencies and governments must co-operate to apply an ecosystem philosophy and principles.

Since the beginning of its work, it has been clear to the Commission that applying an ecosystem approach to restoring and regenerating the Greater Toronto Bioregion requires new thinking and new mechanisms for developing and implementing public policy. It is also clear to the Commission, and to many deputants who appeared before it, that the old ways of finding and funding solutions are no longer sufficient to deal with problems in this increasingly urbanized region.

During the course of its hearings, for example, the Commission heard from a variety of sources, including municipalities, about the inability of the present land-use planning process to incorporate environmental concerns. As Mayor Marie Hubbard, chairperson of the Durham Regional Planning Committee, told the Commission, "the *Planning Act*...has a number of areas where the environmental issues slide through the cracks during the process of applications...."

New methods of dealing with problems should reflect broad, integrated, regional thinking. We cannot afford to ignore the threads that knit the natural environment and the economy into the social fabric, to give us the urban setting in which almost four million Ontarians make their homes today. The new thinking should cut across both traditional boundaries and established jurisdictions if truly sustainable solutions are to be found.

The Commission is encouraged by several initiatives that have brought together the common interests of municipalities and the Province. The newly established Heads of Council Committee and the Greater Toronto Co-ordinating Committee are two examples of a collaborative partnership through which the regional and local municipalities and the Province can shape the urban future of the GTA.

The federal government has participated in a number of significant joint endeavours recently: its prompt support of the Royal Commission's first interim report; its participation in the environmental audit of the East Bayfront and Port Industrial Area lands; its initiative with respect to federal land management in the Toronto area; and its continuous support of the work of the International Joint Commission are to be applauded. Municipalities are also taking initiatives to adopt the ecosystem approach — for example, Metropolitan Toronto is also using this approach for its new Waterfront Plan.

Now, we need to determine how an ecosystem approach can help us find solutions to common problems. We need to pursue opportunities and establish mechanisms that make our provincial and municipal institutions and the federal framework respond to the trans-boundary pressures and stresses in the ecosystem.

It is the Commission's view that this process of bringing governments and people together must begin with the Government of Ontario. The Province should recognize the Toronto Area Waterfront, from Burlington to Newcastle, as a Provincial Resource and commit itself to a policy and program of waterfront regeneration. The representatives of government and government agencies, and the scores of interest groups and individuals who came before the Commission — and who consistently called for strong provincial leadership, collaboration and, resources on which new provincial-municipal partnerships could be constructed — would applaud and support such a declaration.

The provincial commitment would consist of the following:

~ adoption of the ecosystem approach as described in this report;
~ a waterfront regeneration policy based on principles articulated in Chapter 2 of this report;
~ provincial-municipal Waterfront Partnership Agreements, established to ensure consistent purpose and implementation;
~ a financial and resource regime to support the implementation of these Waterfront Partnership Agreements.

The agreements would be created across the waterfront, where appropriate, and up the river valleys, as necessary. While there would obviously be common elements among them, the exact form, nature, composition, and time-frame of the agreements would, of course, depend on the issues being addressed and the regeneration opportunities being pursued in each municipality.

Among the elements that the Royal Commission would recommend be included in the agreements are the following:

~ incorporation of waterfront plans in official plans;
~ provision for a Waterfront Trail with links to river valleys and ravines;
~ provision for water quality and waste-water Remedial Action Plans (RAPs);
~ use of sewer by-laws, based on the Province's model by-law;
~ protection of wetland and other environmentally significant areas;
~ provision of public open space on the waterfront;
~ provision of public transit, road, pedestrian, bicycle, and water access to and along the waterfront;
~ application of provincial Affordable Housing policy requirements in projects on or close to the waterfront;
~ protection or enhancement of historic and heritage environments, both natural and built;
~ particular projects of special interest to each municipality that would improve the waterfront.

The federal government should also consider participating in these agreements, where appropriate. It now has an outstanding opportunity to apply its commendable commitment to the environment in practical ways. Under the Great Lakes Water Quality Agreement, Canada and the United States have specific responsibilities for water quality in the Great Lakes, including, of course, Lake Ontario. Canada also has other responsibilities according to federal-provincial agreements, such as the RAPs.

Indeed, the recently released *Fifth Biennial Report on Great Lakes Water Quality (Part II)* contains recommendations for action by the federal government that could provide great impetus for waterfront regeneration in the Toronto area. Moreover, the Government of Canada, which has extensive landholdings and significant jurisdiction on the waterfront, has a role to play that is too often overlooked and underestimated. The ecosystem approach advocated here requires the active, ongoing participation of the federal government and its agencies.

Public support for this collaborative approach is very high. Indeed, it is clear that people are prepared to back a common vision that takes into account the long-term health and well-being of the waterfront and its river valleys. The hundreds of deputants before the Commission bore witness to that fact.

Toronto Island Airport Ferry

They may well be ahead of their governments. Clearly, they want their various levels of government to build on this consensus and move toward restoring the integrity of the waterfront and the ecosystem that sustains and determines it.

Recommendations

1. All federal, provincial, and municipal governments and agencies with an interest in or influence over the waterfront should adopt the ecosystem approach and principles outlined in this report as a basis for planning.

2. The Province should declare the waterfront from Burlington to Newcastle a Provincial Resource, and it should provide leadership, resources, and opportunities for collaboration amongst various parties, in order to integrate planning and programs as part of efforts to regenerate the waterfront.

3. The Province should establish Waterfront Partnership Agreements with municipalities, along the lines recommended in this report.

4. Over the next year, the Province should work with the Commission to review ways in which the philosophy and principles of the ecosystem approach could best be integrated into the *Planning Act* and other relevant provincial legislation, as it affects the Greater Toronto Bioregion.

5. The Province should encourage and assist in forming a citizens' coalition for the waterfront, to provide research and advocacy on behalf of waterfront users, and to help ensure that issues that cross traditional jurisdictional boundaries are addressed.

   People involved in RAP processes could form the core of this waterfront coalition, but special efforts should also be made to involve the broader constituency represented by such groups as the Centre for the Great Lakes, the Federation of Ontario Naturalists, and the Canadian Environmental Law Association. The coalition might also sponsor local forums in appropriate areas, such as the Toronto Outer Harbour.

   To establish the coalition, the Province should help fund an organizing conference and assist in determining an ongoing financing formula, based on a mix of private and public funding.

2. Waterfront Trail

A Green Strategy for the Greater Toronto Waterfront: Background and Issues, the Commission's Publication No. 8, suggested that a Waterfront Trail should connect the various facilities and green spaces along the shore. In the excellent tradition of such notable pathways as the Adirondack Trail and the Bruce Trail, a Lake Ontario Waterfront Trail could make people aware of the connectedness of the features along the shore. By tying together the often disparate attractions of the waterfront, the trail would help create a sense of community stewardship that is essential to the success of the ecosystem approach.

The trail would also become a symbol of the importance the Province places on the waterfront, and its determination to manage the waterfront in an integrated, ecosystem-based manner.

The trail concept was well received by deputants at the Commission hearings: most agreed that a continuous Waterfront Trail was not only feasible (although difficult in spots), but highly desirable. In some municipalities, trails already exist, such as the Martin Goodman Trail across much of the City of Toronto waterfront. In others, trails are being created, including a system of bicycle paths in Burlington and proposed walkways in Oshawa. The Waterfront Trail would integrate existing sections into a cohesive and more useful whole.

At its ends, the Waterfront Trail should link to the Bruce Trail and the Ganaraska Trail, two long-distance footpaths. Along its course, it should also be linked with trail systems extending up the associated river valleys to and along the Oak Ridges Moraine, as proposed in MTRCA's Greenspace Strategy.

In essence, such a system would cast a green net over the Greater Toronto Area, making the public open spaces far more accessible and attractive. Residents and visitors alike would be able to use the trail system for a few spare moments on their lunch hour, for a pleasant Sunday afternoon or for a vigorous end-to-end jaunt. Continuity is important — not only should there be physical continuity of the trail, but a common logo, design standards and signage should be used to identify the trail throughout.

Within that continuity, however, the system should take full advantage of the diversity within the Greater Toronto Bioregion. The trail could be set in shaded ravines, wind-blown shores, quiet streets, and busy commercial centres. It might be asphalt or gravel, bark chips or natural surface, depending on the location and intended use.

Trail uses could vary: walkers, joggers, hikers in most places, a separate path for bicycles for pleasure or commuting where appropriate, and trails for equestrians in suitable areas, as well as provisions for the disabled, could be accommodated.

In many parts, the system should be buttressed by corridors of green space, both to make the trail experience more pleasant and to protect and maintain the environment on a local scale. Like the greenways which are emerging in the United States, these corridors should be designed to emphasize links among larger attractions, and to weave threads of green into the community fabric.

In more urban sections, the trail should be designed not just for recreation, but as a transportation corridor, and as a safe and convenient alternative to driving for those who want to walk or cycle to work or shopping facilities. This role has been more fully recognized in other jurisdictions: in Britain, for example, developing and maintaining an extensive system of footpaths is the responsibility of roads departments, rather than of parks or recreation authorities. The same assignment of responsibilities could be considered here for trails outside park areas.

The Waterfront Trail should also direct attention to the heritage elements of the waterfront area, both cultural and natural. Heritage considerations should play a major role in both the design and the location of the trail, and in the way it is promoted and described in guidebooks and literature. For example, the trail could be a vehicle to interpret the geological processes visible at the Scarborough Bluffs, and could use signage or interpretive materials to inform people about the industrial heritage of Toronto Harbour. Perhaps the historic parts of downtown Toronto — Queen's Park, Toronto's city halls, University Avenue, the St. Lawrence Market, and other memorable places — could be incorporated to enhance the heritage aspect of the trail.

The idea would also make sense in other cities, towns, and villages along the waterfront. For example, the trail could pass by the Thomas Merrick House at Lakeside Park in Oakville (which recreates the life of a family in 1830); the Guild Inn Estate in Scarborough (to allow interested users to view the art works on display there); and a 300-year-old tree on the bluff east of the Rouge River mouth in Pickering.

A number of barriers to a continuous trail along the waterfront must be overcome. In some places, bridges will be needed over river mouths; footbridges are already planned over the Credit River, Mimico Creek, Humber River, and Duffin Creek. The trail will have to loop inland in places where marshlands and embayments create natural barriers along the shore, to avoid undue pressure on sensitive wildlife habitats. It will also have to be routed inland to bypass major industries such as generating stations and quarries.

In existing residential areas, the trail will often have to go along quiet streets, linking existing parklands on the shore. In some places, waterfront properties can be gradually acquired to create windows to the lake. Elsewhere, redevelopment can be used to gain shoreline strips to be incorporated into the trail system, as now happens in Oakville and some other municipalities.

It may occasionally be essential to acquire properties to provide links while avoiding busy roads. In order to help achieve continuity, the trail should be designed to make full use of existing public lands, such as water and sewer facility lands, as appropriate links.

Some barriers may be overcome only in the long term. Planning for the Waterfront Trail can take that reality into account by specifying both a final and an interim route, which would allow necessary connections to be completed in the short term.

In the past, the planning, developing, promoting, and maintaining of long-distance trails in Ontario have been carried out, in the main, by volunteer, non-government groups.

Few places in the world better illustrate a far-reaching chain of ecological effects on the environment caused by human activity than the Great Lakes. The interconnections between the physical features and living things are such that in the Great Lakes, when any one characteristic of water quality is altered, then change reverberates throughout the ecological system.

Theberge, J. B. 1989. "Changes in water characteristics and aquatic life." In *Legacy: the natural heritage of Ontario*, editor J. B. Theberge. 323. Toronto: McClelland and Stewart.

The provincial government has become increasingly involved in securing the Bruce Trail route in recent years, as part of the Niagara Escarpment land-acquisition program. However, the leadership and the legwork of the non-government Bruce Trail Association are still essential to success.

The Commission has commented on the desirability of having a membership association to support a Waterfront Trail. Such an association could play a pivotal role in planning, promoting, advocating, and even being involved in some aspects of constructing and maintaining the trail. However, because of the high density of people and development along the waterfront, development and maintenance of a trail there will require a greater degree of provincial and municipal involvement.

~~~~~~~~~~

Recommendations

6. The Province should plan, co-ordinate, and implement a Waterfront Trail from Burlington to Newcastle (as shown conceptually on Map 2), to be completed by 1993 to celebrate both the bicentennial of the founding of York and the centennial of the Ontario provincial parks system.

7. The Province should provide financial and technical assistance for the founding and early operations of a Waterfront Trail Association, to support its involvement in planning and implementing a Waterfront Trail.

8. The Province should require all waterfront municipalities and all provincial agencies to incorporate the Waterfront Trail route into plans affecting their waterfront areas.

3. Oak Ridges Moraine

During the course of the Commission's hearings, deputants repeatedly stressed their conviction that the waterfront cannot be considered in isolation from its bioregion. The links are most strongly expressed in relation to water quality issues, but the waterfront is also tied to its hinterland, especially through the valley systems, in terms of wildlife movement and recreational uses.

In particular, citizen groups, conservation authorities, and municipalities came forward to emphasize the natural and scenic significance of the Oak Ridges Moraine, and to urge that it be protected. Of special significance to this Commission is the role of the moraine as the source of a great deal of the streamflow in the rivers feeding into the waterfront. Because the headwater springs along the edges of the moraine tap into a vast underground reservoir of groundwater encased in the gravels of the moraine's landforms, the streams there are cool and unpolluted.

Forty-two streams along the moraine support healthy trout populations, a good indicator of their quality. This reliable, clean source of water for communities and rivers alike is a vital asset in the struggle to restore water quality in the Greater Toronto Area.

Katherine Guselle of Save the Ganaraska Again (SAGA) emphasized to the Commission the strong connections between the moraine and the waterfront:

> It is fair to say that the ecological health of the extensive waterfront you are studying will depend in great measure on the continued health of the undisturbed natural headwaters and watersheds, such as the Ganaraska River, that drain the south slope of the Oak Ridges Moraine.

Many of the deputants made reference to *The Adequacy of the Existing Environmental Planning and Approvals Process for the Ganaraska Watershed*, Report No. 38 of the Ontario Environmental Assessment

SAVE THE OAK RIDGES MORAINE

S.T.O.R.M.

Box 2209, Station B, Richmond Hill, Ontario L4E 1A4

Advisory Committee (EAAC), which made a series of recommendations about planning and development on the moraine. The report obviously struck a chord: deputants were virtually unanimous in praising and endorsing it. The Commission heard many citations of inappropriate or poorly planned development on the moraine, and of widespread threats from land speculation and gravel extraction.

The Commission was also told that the existing land-use control system is inadequate in taking into account cumulative effects of development on the environment, or in preventing destruction of natural features as part of development. Many deputants echoed this conclusion of the EAAC report:

> The existing land-use planning and approval process in Ontario is inadequate to the task of maintaining social and ecological quality in the face of development pressures.

This Commission recognizes that the Oak Ridges Moraine has been studied in more depth by Ron Kanter, MPP, whose recommendations address many of the concerns about the future of the moraine that were discussed with the Commission. It is clear, however, that preserving the Oak Ridges Moraine is central to an ecosystem approach to management of the waterfront. It is equally clear that the existing patchwork of municipal, conservation authority, and provincial programs will lead only to a progressive and severe decline in the quality of the moraine and associated rivers. In the words of Dorothy Izzard of Save The Oak Ridges Moraine (STORM) coalition:

> If our precarious ground water supply and base flow level in a significantly populated area of south central Ontario is to be maintained, a strong provincial policy with rigidly enforced land-use controls on the Moraine is vital and urgently required.

This Commission shares that sense of urgency. Most of the moraine can still be preserved as an outstanding ecological and recreational landscape, but only as a result of firm and timely provincial action now, before further opportunities are lost. The Province needs to take steps to reduce development pressures in the short term, and to provide immediate protection for such critical areas as wetlands, valleylands, and significant natural areas.

The development of an improved information base on the groundwater hydrology of the moraine, along with effective provincial or conservation authority actions to protect that groundwater resource, should be considered matters of urgency. Integration of protective strategies for the moraine into municipal planning documents should be mandatory.

~~~~~~~~~~

Recommendations

9. The Province should take immediate steps to preserve the ecological, scenic, and recreational significance of the Oak Ridges Moraine, and to ensure that future land use in the moraine does not result in cumulative impairment of the ecological quality of downstream rivers or the waterfront.

10. In view of the number of jurisdictions and the complexity of issues involved, a discrete planning group with a clear provincial mandate, working in a limited time-frame, should be established to:
    a) identify conservation priorities for wetlands, valleylands, and significant natural landscapes;
    b) document the extent and characteristics of groundwater resources;
    c) identify significant scenic and cultural landscapes and potential trail locations;
    d) analyse the cumulative impact of various types of development activity;
    e) identify the appropriate type, scale, density, and location of future development;

f) identify suitable mechanisms to achieve conservation and land-use objectives on the moraine;
g) analyse the best means of implementing a conservation plan for the moraine.

11. While the planning study is under way, the Province should declare a Provincial Interest in the moraine under the *Planning Act*, in order to protect the integrity of the planning process and to control development pressures on the moraine.

4. Water Quality

The problems of water quality in the Greater Toronto Bioregion are well known: they include lake and river waters polluted with nutrients, bacteria, organic chemicals, and heavy metals; beaches closed for swimming; wildlife habitat degraded or lost to development; contaminated bottom sediments; and persistent toxic chemicals in aquatic biota.

The last problem is the most disturbing, because wildlife are indicators of ecosystem health — the canaries in our coal mine. In the Great Lakes Basin, some 16 species near the top of the food chain have suffered population declines since the 1950s, as the result of exposure to persistent toxic chemicals.

It is obvious to the Royal Commission that restoration of water quality is one of the major environmental issues facing residents and governments in the bioregion, and that regeneration of the waterfront and the bioregion is not possible without clean water.

The importance of our water resources was stated very succinctly in the *Fifth Biennial Report on Great Lakes Water Quality*, released by the International Joint Commission in the spring of 1990:

> The Great Lakes are an immeasurably important resource. They are ecologically important in their own right: the home of many species (some now

extinct) and one of the greatest reservoirs of fresh water in the world with all its hydrological, meteorological, geological and biological implications. They are also the economic and social lifeblood of a large part of our two countries. They provide drinking and irrigation water, fisheries and wildlife habitat, transportation, power, processing water, recreational opportunities and many other services to humans living in and outside of the Great Lakes Basin.

Cleaning up the waters of the bioregion is a complex task, with technical, social, and economic implications. But inaction, too, has profound implications. To quote the International Joint Commission again:

Despite the significance of the Great Lakes and our collective rhetoric to restore and enhance them, we as a society continue to mortgage their future by poisoning, suffocating and otherwise threatening them because of insufficient knowledge, other priorities and short-sightedness. What our generation has failed to realize is that, what we are doing to the Great Lakes, we are doing to ourselves and to our children.

Using an ecosystem approach recognizes that cleaning up the waters in the Greater Toronto Bioregion is linked to cleaning up Lake Ontario, which is in turn linked to remediation and preventive measures throughout the Great Lakes Basin to restore water quality. It will require concerted and collaborative efforts by all levels of government in Canada and the United States, and will involve the public and private sectors.

This co-ordinated effort must begin now, and must focus on the goal of "zero discharge": stopping the flow of persistent toxic substances into Lake Ontario and the other Great Lakes. The purpose is not just to protect aquatic wildlife — humans (35 million of them) live in the Great Lakes Basin too.

They drink its water, eat its fish, and breathe its air.

The International Joint Commission has concluded that:

When available data on fish, birds, reptiles and small mammals are considered along with human research, the Commission must conclude that there is a threat to the health of our children emanating from our exposure to persistent toxic substances, even at very low ambient levels.

LAKE ONTARIO TOXICS MANAGEMENT PLAN

In recognizing environmental problems throughout the Great Lakes, governments around the basin are developing lake-wide remedial plans under the guidance of the International Joint Commission. The plan for Lake Ontario, the most contaminated of the Great Lakes, is the Lake Ontario Toxics Management Plan (LOTMP), which is being developed by the governments of Canada and the United States, the State of New York, and the Province of Ontario.

The plan will address critical pollutants on a lake-wide basis, including inputs from atmospheric sources, direct and indirect industrial sources, municipalities, agricultural activities, and contaminated sediments. The Niagara River is considered the greatest source of pollution in Lake Ontario. Other sources of contaminants include the discharges from the Greater Toronto Area, Hamilton Harbour, and many rivers in the Lake Ontario watershed.

The problems in some of these regional sources are being addressed by Remedial Action Plans being developed for eight sites around Lake Ontario, one of which is the Metropolitan Toronto Waterfront.

Of the five lake-wide management plans being developed, apparently the Lake Ontario Plan has so far received the most attention and effort. However, it is proceeding slowly, and has had a very low profile and little or no formal public input.

Public support for cleaning up Lake Ontario is essential for success, but the general public is not aware of the LOTMP, and does not have access to information on pollution loadings from both sides of the border. Because Ontario municipalities will have to deliver on the strategies being developed in the LOTMP, they must be aware of the plan and involved in its development. This is not now the case.

Cleaning up Lake Ontario will be costly, and the toughest challenges may be social and economic, rather than technical. It will take considerable time to develop and implement solutions — and it could be decades before restoration is complete. In recognition of the urgent need for collaborative efforts to restore water quality, the following recommendations of the Royal Commission are addressed to all levels of government — federal, provincial, regional, and municipal.

Recommendations

12. The federal government and the Province of Ontario should establish a process that ensures the Canadian public is fully involved and consulted in the way the Lake Ontario Toxics Management Plan is developed and remediation priorities are set under it.

13. The federal and provincial governments should establish a process for informing and involving municipalities around Lake Ontario in developing the LOTMP.

14. Subsequent to the above, the International Joint Commission and the four LOTMP parties should review progress on the LOTMP and establish priorities for remedial strategies to be undertaken on a lake-wide basis, taking into account the wishes of the public as expressed in the previously recommended consultations.

15. The IJC and the four LOTMP parties should publish regular reports on the progress being made to restore the environmental integrity of Lake Ontario.

MISA

Ontario's Municipal-Industrial Strategy for Abatement (MISA) program was set up in 1986 by the Ministry of the Environment to "stop pollution at the source" by reducing the loading of toxic chemicals from nine industrial sectors and from municipalities. The ultimate goal of MISA is the virtual elimination of discharges of persistent toxic substances into Ontario's waters. The approach to be used is to legislate the use of best available technology at source: i.e., where the toxic is created, used or disposed of.

The industrial portion of the MISA program deals with large industries that discharge directly into Ontario's waters — industrial sectors such as petroleum, pulp and paper, and iron and steel. The regulations to be developed for these industrial sectors may not have a considerable direct impact on the Greater Toronto Area — apparently there are no direct industrial dischargers along the waterfront, for example. However, the benefits of MISA will be felt here strongly as industries upstream in the Great Lakes reduce their loadings of persistent toxic chemicals into rivers and the lakes.

The municipal part of MISA will affect the Greater Toronto Area directly. As many as 6,000 industries and commercial establishments in the GTA discharge into systems leading to the 11 sewage treatment plants (STPs) in the area. An estimated 3,000 of these establishments discharge organic chemicals and heavy metals into the sewers — from electroplaters or photofinishers, product manufacturers or autobody shops, or from any industry that produces small amounts of toxic waste and dumps them down the drain.

Port of Toronto, MT35, Keating Channel dredging

Sewer dumping of toxic chemicals (from residents as well as industries) is responsible for about 90 per cent of the total load of chemicals reaching the Greater Toronto Waterfront. These toxic chemicals can interfere in the normal functioning of STPs by killing the bacteria that break down septic wastes. They can also cause corrosion in pipes and sewage treatment plants, and can pose a health hazard to STP workers. And because STPs are not designed to treat or remove chemicals, most chemicals dumped into sewers pass directly through to receiving waters.

The chemicals and metals removed by the STPs remain in the sewage sludge and then become an air pollution problem when they are incinerated. (Most sludge in the GTA is incinerated because it is too contaminated to spread on agricultural land.)

The MISA Sewer Use Control Program for the municipal sector, due in 1994, will set tough new standards for sewer discharge of organic chemicals and heavy metals. These will force pre-treatment and/or reduction of the problem at source, using the best available technologies. These technologies could range from end-of-the-pipe treatments (like reverse osmosis to remove metals from wastewater) or closed-loop systems (where no discharge is needed).

Applying the MISA Sewer Use Control Program will result in dramatic improvements in the quality of sludge and effluents from STPs and, in turn, in local air, water, and sediment quality. Although the MISA regulations are not expected until 1994, some municipalities are already taking action. For example, Metropolitan Toronto has, as an important interim step, moved to implement a "model sewer use by-law" developed by the Province; it will significantly decrease the loading of persistent toxic chemicals into Metropolitan Toronto's sewage treatment system.

Recommendation

16. The regions of Peel, Halton, York, and Durham should implement a "model sewer use by-law" similar to that adopted by Metropolitan Toronto, as an interim step until the MISA Sewer Use Control Program is in place. These sewer use by-laws should become part of the Waterfront Partnership Agreements developed for the regions.

SEDIMENTS

Even after the Metro Toronto RAP and MISA programs are fully implemented — five, ten, 20 years from now — the historical legacy of past activities will remain in the form of toxic chemicals, metals, and nutrients in bottom sediments. Unless these sediments are treated, they will continue to be a problem in the years to come, and many deputants at the Royal Commission hearings expressed concerns about them.

These problems exist all along the Greater Toronto Waterfront and at virtually all of the 42 Areas of Concern around the Great Lakes designated by the IJC. They are of concern because toxics and nutrients can become resuspended in the water column when disturbed by dredging or lakefilling. Organic chemicals and heavy metals are also taken up by bottom-dwelling organisms and can thus enter the food chain, eventually affecting humans.

The Commission believes that a complete evaluation of sediment quality along the entire waterfront is required. Such a study would provide the public and clean-up agencies with information that is vital to the ecosystem approach to remediation, and would offer data against which remedial progress could be measured. Such a study would also serve as a model for similar programs elsewhere around the Great Lakes.

The Commission also believes that vital work needs to be done on possible remedial options for contaminated sediments. At present, most remedial action consists of dredging and disposal, options that move the problem around rather than solving it.

Recommendations

17. The Province of Ontario should conduct a study to determine the overall chemical and bacteriological quality of bottom sediments along the GTA waterfront. Such a study should include geographic trends, effects on biota, and options for remediation.

18. The federal and provincial governments should fund research on technically sound methods of sediment rehabilitation and should focus such research on remediating the polluted sediments found in virtually all Great Lakes Areas of Concern.

THE METRO TORONTO REMEDIAL ACTION PLAN

As one of 42 Areas of Concern designated by the International Joint Commission,

the Metropolitan Toronto waterfront is the subject of a Remedial Action Plan (RAP) being developed by the federal and provincial governments. The goal of the RAP is to restore local water quality, to make it "swimmable, drinkable and fishable".

The Royal Commission's first interim report, released in 1989, included comments on the RAP. While the Commission supported the goals of the RAP, it felt that, at the time, the process being used to develop and implement it had problems.

As part of the process, the RAP team released a *Draft Discussion Paper on Remedial Options* for public comment immediately prior to the Commission's hearings on environment and health in May 1990. The discussion document identified a range of options and the associated costs for restoring water quality on the waterfront. As such, it is a valuable technical paper.

It would appear, however, that there are still problems with the RAP process used to date. At the hearings, a number of deputants made comments on the RAP discussion paper, criticizing it as being confusing and difficult to read. Therefore, it is unlikely to generate much discussion from the public at large.

Sarah Miller, of the City's Waterfront Remedial Action Plan Committee, pointed out that the next stage of the RAP process — ranking preferred remedial options — was impossible to achieve because there was no link made between water quality goals and remedial options. She suggested that there was too much emphasis on "end-of-pipe" treatment and dilution, and not enough on preventing problems from occurring.

Another concern expressed at the hearings in May, as it had been in the Commission's 1989 environment and health hearings, is how slowly the Toronto RAP is being developed. Subsequently, the RAP Public Advisory Committee (PAC) said it was concerned with the way it is isolated from the RAP writing team, and the lack of funds given it to carry out its work.

All of those who commented on the RAP mentioned implementation difficulties because of the many jurisdictions involved. For example, although it is a member of the RAP's Technical Advisory Committee (TAC), part of the RAP's development, the City of Toronto's Public Works Department does not currently consider the RAP in its planning or in setting its priorities. Similar comments were received from the City of Etobicoke. To overcome the fragmentation of jurisdictions and ensure implementation of the final Remedial Action Plan, a fully funded public advisory or watchdog committee was suggested. In Sarah Miller's words:

> I think the pivotal point around which the public is going to support or reject the RAP process will be in the support that the process gives to the role of continuing public involvement and expanded public committees for each RAP area. If this continuance in support is denied the public, their interest is going to wane and we can surely know that the RAPs are going to languish. Politicians are going to change, bureaucrats are going to move from one agency to another; the only continuum, I think, that RAPs have is the public interest and that has to be given precedence.

Over the last year, the Commission has worked closely with both levels of government on the Remedial Action Plan and some progress has been achieved as the result of this co-operation. However, the Commission believes that the hurdle of jurisdictional fragmentation can be overcome only if remedial measures are implemented by partnerships on a watershed basis.

In the Humber River watershed, for example, there are three regions, ten municipalities, and 515,000 people. In such a situation, one municipality acting alone can achieve little. Clean-up of the rivers in the watershed will require the co-operation and involvement of all governments and residents.

Recommendations

19. The federal and provincial governments should modify the RAP process by elevating each municipality from being one of many stakeholders, to being a joint partner in developing and implementing the RAP. Using the watershed approach, all municipalities within a given watershed should be asked to collaborate on the RAP.

20. The federal and provincial governments should rewrite the *Draft Discussion Paper on Remedial Options* as soon as possible, in order to make it more readily understandable to the general public, to provide information on a watershed basis, and to establish clear links between the RAP goals, the impaired uses, and the remedial options.

21. The federal and provincial governments should provide funds and resources to the RAP Public Advisory Committee to allow it to function effectively. Funds should include *per diems* for participants in meetings.

22. The current "caucuses" that are part of the RAP public involvement program are organized on a sectoral basis. The federal and provincial governments should also organize them to bring the sectors together on a watershed basis.

23. The Remedial Action Plan, when finalized, should become part of the Waterfront Partnership Agreements previously recommended by the Royal Commission, negotiated for the rivers draining into the Metropolitan Toronto waterfront.

WATER QUALITY AND CONSUMPTION

Since the early 1980s, public concern about water has centred on quality issues — the quality of drinking water, toxics in bottom sediments, high bacterial counts at beaches, and contaminants in aquatic wildlife. Some deputants at the environment and health hearings argued, however, that water quantity is as pressing a concern as water quality, and furthermore, that it is integral to water quality issues. In other words, the argument is that water quality cannot be restored without broad strategies to conserve water.

As a society, we have become accustomed to using vast amounts of cheap water for washing, bathing, and gardening, as well as for commercial and industrial uses. Environment Canada estimates that water consumption increased by 54 per cent between 1972 and 1981, while the population of Canada increased by only about five per cent. Most residents of the GTA pay a flat yearly rate for water, and only 30 per cent of houses in the area have water meters. Residents blithely water lawns and wash cars, unaware of (and protected from) the costs of their actions. But there are hidden environmental costs to water use — costs that are not reflected in water bills and are borne by the environment.

Every litre of water pumped and treated for residential, commercial or industrial use becomes wastewater that then has to be treated at a sewage treatment plant. In addition to passing through toxic chemicals, (which they are not designed to treat), STPs discharge high amounts of nutrients into surface waters. During major rainstorms, STPs regularly bypass partially treated sewage and stormwater from combined sewer overflows, which causes degradation of lakes and rivers.

The usual engineering solution has been to increase STP size to deal with increasing volumes of wastewater; deputants at the hearings argued that water conservation strategies to decrease the use of water should be adopted by municipalities in the GTA.

The 1987 Federal Water Policy had, as its overall objective, "to encourage the use of freshwater in an efficient and equitable manner consistent with the social, economic and environmental needs of present and future generations". This underlies a commitment to promote the wise and efficient management and use of water and, in doing so, to protect and enhance the quality of water resources. Deputants made the case that comprehensive municipal water conservation strategies (including realistic pricing per litre for users) would induce a decline in water use of as much as 20 per cent or more. In turn, that would mean lower levels of wastewater production, and better control of effluents (thereby reducing the pollution from STPs). Moreover, capital costs for new or expanded sewage treatment facilities and utility costs would be reduced.

Realistic pricing and water metering would generate greater revenue for municipalities, revenue that could be used for upgrading aging sewage treatment infrastructures or for local efforts such as a RAP to improve water quality.

Recommendation

24. The Province, through an appropriate designated agency, and in collaboration with the Canadian Water and Wastewater Association, should conduct a case study to examine the extent of the relationship between water quality and the volume of water used by the population of the Greater Toronto Area. The study should also assess conservation methods (including pricing) and how they contribute to improved water quality.

5. Lakefill

In its 1989 interim report, the Royal Commission made a series of recommendations concerning lakefill along the Metropolitan Toronto waterfront. While recognizing that some exemptions might be necessary for extraordinary projects, the Commission recommended a moratorium on all new lakefilling until a comprehensive provincial policy was developed, with more restrictive open-water disposal guidelines being applied to lakefill projects currently under way. In addition, the Commission recommended that, once the moratorium was lifted, all individual lakefilling projects, including private-sector developments, should be subject to thorough environmental appraisals.

One year having passed since these recommendations were made, this is an opportune moment at which to comment briefly on the progress that has been made to date.

The Commission recognizes that many lakefill projects developed in the past were of benefit to the public. Undeniably, some of the most attractive features of the waterfront, including the Toronto Harbour, Harbourfront, the Leslie Street Spit, the extension of the Toronto Islands (which were a natural peninsula in the first place), Exhibition Place, Ontario Place, and a host of parks across the waterfront, are the result of lakefill.

Lakefill can be beneficial in a situation where a compelling public purpose makes it necessary to restore or rejuvenate an inhospitable shoreline. Nevertheless, the

Tommy Thompson Park under development

The Province has yet to release the results of its review of methods and quality controls to be applied to lakefill projects and has not imposed a moratorium on new lakefill projects. However, the Commission is not aware of any new lakefill projects along the Metropolitan Toronto waterfront, although several, including the East Point Park proposal, are in various stages of the approval process.

On the matter of lakefill quality, in March 1990, the Metropolitan Toronto and Region Conservation Authority (MTRCA) enhanced its Improved Lakefill Quality Control Program by implementing open-water disposal guidelines for all fill dumped into the lake at MTRCA projects.

trade-off has been to obtain these benefits at the expense of potentially damaging, long-term environmental change. The problems include:

~ modification of coastal processes which, left untouched, normally disperse and transport wastes from other sources away from the nearshore area;

~ lakefill as a direct source of contaminants, contributing to their accumulation in sediments;

~ the lack of definitive guidelines on sediment quality, including acceptable treatment of in-place contaminated sediments;

~ lack of assurance that the cumulative environmental impact associated with lakefill quality and design will be adequately dealt with in the environmental assessment process.

The Commission still believes that a comprehensive lakefill policy is both necessary and desirable, and that such a policy ought to be developed and applied to the entire Greater Toronto Waterfront. Planned and proposed lakefill projects across the waterfront (excluding some of the larger, more speculative proposals) currently involve more than 250 hectares (620 acres); taken together, they are estimated to require more than ten million cubic metres of fill.

The various effects and the cumulative impact of these projects are not fully understood at present. Lakefill has been carried out in other parts of the Great Lakes Basin with more sensitivity to these issues than has been shown in Ontario.

If lakefill is to continue to be permitted, it must be governed by a stronger set of policies than now exists. In the next phase of its work, the Commission proposes to examine the issue of appropriate lakefill policies in general and as they could be applied in relation to a specific area of shoreline in need of rehabilitation. It will work with the Government of Ontario, landowners, and interest groups to identify practices that should govern lakefilling activities in the future, and to find alternate solutions for the problem of handling excavate.

~~~~~~

Recommendations

25. The Province should bring forward comprehensive lakefill policies for public review as soon as possible. The policies should require thorough environmental appraisal of all individual lakefill projects, and of their cumulative

effects, across the Greater Toronto Waterfront. Until such policies are in place, there should be a moratorium on new lakefilling.

26. Open-water disposal guidelines should be adopted for current lakefill projects.

6. Restoring Fish, Wildlife and Natural Areas

As recognized in the principles discussed in Chapter 2, the diversity of species is a hallmark of a healthy ecosystem. Along the waterfront and throughout the Greater Toronto Bioregion, declines in the diversity and abundance of wild species are a prime symptom of an ecosystem under stress.

If we are to reverse this trend, several steps must be taken. First, we need to increase our understanding of the distribution and patterns of decline now occurring in species along the waterfront. Second, we must develop effective strategies to preserve those species under the greatest threat, and to restore original species now missing from waterfront ecosystems. Finally, we need to develop new means of increasing awareness and appreciation of fish, wildlife, and other species, as part of the ecosystem, in order to generate the public support necessary for implementing effective restoration measures.

Over the past decade, the Province has developed an ecological approach to managing aquatic habitats, through its Strategic Plans for Ontario Fisheries II. The ways in which terrestrial wildlife is managed have been changed more slowly to respond to new realities, although the current deliberations of the Ontario Wildlife Working Group hold some hope for a more enlightened approach to ecologically based management in future. In the past, conservation of rare plants and other forms of natural life has generally been accorded a low priority by provincial agencies.

27. The Province, in concert with local agencies and volunteer groups, should develop a co-operative strategy to:
    a) collect more detailed information on the distribution and abundance of native species along the waterfront;
    b) identify a series of ecosystem indicator species, co-ordinated with a program of periodic monitoring, to detect changes in species diversity and population levels;
    c) prepare and implement active strategies to preserve and manage species known to be provincially or regionally rare or threatened.

28. Environment Canada's Canadian Wildlife Service, working in conjunction with provincial wildlife officials, waterfront park managers, and interest groups, should extend its population control program for giant Canada geese along the entire Metropolitan Toronto Waterfront.

29. The Ontario Ministry of Natural Resources should develop plans to create a significant shore-based sport fishery along the waterfront, using a combination of selective stocking, habitat enhancement, and improved access at fishing piers and boat-launch ramps. Joint federal, provincial, and municipal involvement should be sought for implementing these plans, which should be designed to establish naturally sustaining communities of native species.

30. Conservation authorities and municipalities should examine ways to expand birdwatching activities along the waterfront, especially during migration and winter months, by providing improved access, facilities, programs, and events.

The work of conservation will never end. Perhaps most conservationists are men of whom the prophet Joel wrote: 'Your old men shall dream dreams, your young men shall see visions.' Perhaps conservationists will always be setting aside lands so that they will not be all absorbed by the throbbing life of urban expansion, so that always some lands will be retained as oases of peace for those who toil in the city, so that in the years to come these valleys may echo with the laughter of children, so that young people may witness the ever-recurring miracle of spring, and so that parents may enjoy the solace of nature for tired bodies and minds.

Richardson, A. H. 1974. *Conservation by the people: the history of the conservation movement in Ontario to 1970*, xi. Toronto: Conservation Authorities of Ontario.

7. Trees in the City

In their natural condition, the lands along the north shore of Lake Ontario were clad in mixed forest. Replacing trees — singly, in clusters or in corridors — is one of the single most important facets of restoring the ecosystem within the city and the bioregion.

It is impossible to overestimate the value of a tree. As Michael Hough, landscape architect, commented at the Commission's hearings:

> Forests protect watersheds. They stabilize slopes, minimize erosion, reduce sediment inputs into streams and maintain the quality and temperature of water. In the hilly uplands of a watershed, where water sources originate, forest vegetation generally influences the movement of water from the atmosphere to the earth and back again. It performs a vital function of maintaining stream flows and reducing peaks and potential flooding but sustaining flows in dry periods.

CN Tower from the Toronto Islands

The first step in urban reforestation must be improved means to protect existing tree cover. Urban trees are frequent victims of air pollution and salt damage — the average life of urban trees is measured in years, rather than decades. Moreover, many trees are lost through the actions of developers.

The Commission heard concerns raised by the Parks and Recreation Federation of Ontario that:

> At the present time, under the *Trees Act* of Ontario, the one piece of legislation from which regional and municipal by-laws flow, municipalities or regional governments cannot prevent the destruction of trees on private property.

Other deputants told stories of developers stripping tree cover from their lands in advance of submitting planning applications — and found there was apparently no way to prevent this abusive practice. Clearly, preventing wholesale destruction of trees is one matter in which municipalities need new legislative and regulatory tools.

The value of planting new trees can be greatly enhanced ecologically if emphasis is given to native species, rather than to exotics introduced from beyond our shores. The Commission was pleased to note that the City of Toronto has begun producing its own native trees for use in the City, but recognizes that finding a supply of most types of native trees and shrubs continues to be a problem in many areas.

Finding suitable locations in which to plant trees should pose few difficulties. A renewed program of tree-planting on urban streets could be one starting point, leading to more liveable and attractive communities for our children. Planting in river valleys and other natural corridors would help enhance the ecological and recreational values in these areas. And planting low-growing shrubs and trees in appropriate locations along the edges of expressways and railway lines would help trap air and water pollutants

and reduce noise levels. Creating urban forests on the edges of urban areas, similar to the model used by the British Countryside Commission, would provide larger areas of habitat and more recreation opportunities.

The Province's recent creation of the Trees Ontario Foundation, to assist in keeping up with demand for tree-planting stock, is just one sign of increased public interest in tree-planting.

Beach and bluffs, east of Port Darlington Harbour

values of trees in urban and near-urban municipalities.

Recommendations

31. The Province should immediately undertake a review of the Ontario *Trees Act*, in conjunction with municipalities and interest groups, to decide how changes should be made to the legislation to ensure that it protects the ecological, aesthetic, and recreational

32. Municipalities and conservation authorities should develop and implement strategies to at least double the number of trees in the waterfront municipalities by the turn of the century. These strategies should seek to create extensive tracts of new community forests, in waterfront areas such as the "urban separator" between Whitby and Oshawa, and at the foot of the Don Valley.

33. The Province should ensure that the Trees Ontario Foundation makes available the widest possible diversity of native tree and shrub species, to encourage ecologically appropriate plantings.

8. Mandate of Conservation Authorities

Few topics elicited such a wide range of views as the activities of conservation authorities across the GTA. The Commission was told that authorities interpret their mandates too broadly or too narrowly; authorities should take a greater or a lesser role in recreation; and that authorities should have the lead role or a very limited role along the waterfront.

As outlined in *A Green Strategy for the Greater Toronto Waterfront: Background and Issues* (Commission Publication No. 8), the roles of conservation authorities specific to the waterfront vary considerably. All five authorities have responsibility for mapping and regulations related to waterfront flooding and erosion control. Beyond this basic duty, their roles in protecting natural habitats and developing recreation along the waterfront depend greatly on local preferences, historical arrangements, and the availability of funding.

The important contributions that Ontario conservation authorities have made in the past are well known. Often hampered by inadequate funding, they have carried out important tasks that have been left undone by other agencies or levels of government. Many people today still know conservation authorities as competent promoters of recreation and conservation programs.

Nevertheless, people are often critical. At least among many of those who appeared before the Commission, there appears to be a crisis in confidence about the role of conservation authorities. People expect that the primary responsibility of conservation authorities is conservation — protecting valleylands and natural areas, taking the lead in restoring water quality, planting trees and shrubs to attract wildlife.

What they see instead is the recreation and development side of conservation authorities: building spits of lakefill into the water, developing marinas and active recreation parks, turning streams into sterile ditches in the name of flood control. Rather than being perceived as passionate defenders of the environment, the authorities are seen as one among any number of despoilers. In Durham Region, that perception has been strengthened by the recent attempt by the Central Lake Ontario Conservation Authority to develop a subdivision on some of its lands.

There are, of course, valid reasons for the way authorities now operate, and no one denies they have achieved tremendous good over the years. However, there is some sense of public disillusionment about their current activities. For example, Helen MacDonald, resident of Newcastle, told the Commission, "... we have to be realistic ... they are flood control and erosion authorities with a little bit of development thrown in on the side." Conservation authorities need public support to operate effectively and may have to adapt their policies to reflect current attitudes, if they hope to maintain it.

Marion Strebig of the Federation of Ontario Naturalists said:

> It made me shudder to think of the conservation authorities in charge of lakefront, because I think they see the lakeshore, not in terms of natural areas, or in terms even of people's enjoyment, but ... like playing with mud pies almost — it's something to play with — see what we can throw out here, and what development we can put here.

Conservation authorities came in for other criticisms as well. Mayor Marie Hubbard of Newcastle stated that the authorities repeatedly offered no objections to developments proposed for sensitive headwaters. She and many others also raised concerns about the system of assigning political appointees to conservation authorities, whose devotion to conservation was likely to be tempered by municipal attitudes that favour more development.

In light of these concerns, the current provincial review of the mandate of conservation authorities is timely. In a speech on 9 April 1990, the Minister of Natural Resources, the Honourable Lyn McLeod, outlined the proposed changes resulting from the work of two committees. She said that one of the proposed reforms would be to distinguish between core and non-core programs of conservation authorities, with only core programs qualifying for MNR transfer grants. Another proposal would reorganize authorities, reducing the number in southern Ontario from 33 to 19. The number of authority board members would also be reduced, although appointments would still be made by municipalities and the Province. Finally, funding arrangements with conservation authorities would be changed.

While such reforms will address some of the concerns raised at the Commission hearings — for example, by giving authorities a clear mandate with respect to regionally significant natural areas — others will not be affected. Clearly, the proposed administrative changes will not transform conservation authorities into the strong defenders of the natural environment that many want them to be.

~~~~

Recommendations

34. The Province should review concerns about the mandate and functioning of conservation authorities raised by deputants before this Commission, in order to determine whether more fundamental reforms are needed as part of the current review.

35. Conservation authorities along the waterfront should retain responsibility for mapping and regulation related to flooding and erosion hazard, and should assume a greater role in protecting and linking natural habitats and in managing watersheds. Funding for these core activities should be provided now as a matter of right, on a matching-formula basis.

36. All other activities related to the waterfront should be subject to negotiations within the context of the Waterfront Partnership Agreements previously recommended in this report; funding should be provided for these activities, to be determined in such negotiations.

9. Urban Form and Structure

In the Greater Toronto Area in the past several years, there has been considerable public discussion and media coverage of issues that relate in one way or another to matters of urban form and structure: congestion and commuting, shortage of affordable housing, lack of parkland and open space, waste disposal, access to the waterfront, strains on the quality of life, reduction of environmental quality, and the shape and size of urban areas.

Those issues will undoubtedly be exacerbated by population growth: provincial estimates expect population increases of about 50 per cent, or two million people, within the next 30 years.

Three major governmental policy initiatives are now emerging and should more sharply define and focus public debate as governments across the region gear themselves to make the key decisions necessary to manage the growth of the region over the next 30 years. The initiatives are: the work of the Greater Toronto Co-ordinating Committee (GTCC), the report of MPP Ron Kanter on the Oak Ridges Moraine and river valleys of the GTA, and the work of the Royal Commission on the Future of the Toronto Waterfront.

The provincial government established the GTCC in 1987 to examine issues that affect all municipalities and regions in the GTA. The committee includes provincial officials, as well as representatives from the five regional municipalities and 30 local municipalities in the GTA.

In June 1990, the Minister of Municipal Affairs released a study of urban structure concepts developed under the auspices of the GTCC detailing three different ways to manage population growth over the next 30 years.

The urbanized area of the GTA totalled 1,500 square kilometres (590 square miles) in 1986. Based on the three urban structures, that area could grow to between 1,890 square kilometres (730 square miles) and 2,400 square kilometres (940 square miles) in the next 30 years.

The study estimates that the cost of this growth would be approximately the same for each of the three concepts, about $79 billion, or approximately $23 billion more than would be spent on urban services in that period if there were no population growth.

The three urban concepts are as follows:

~ The *Spread* model assumes that existing trends would continue and growth would occur largely in the suburban regions, resulting in an urbanized area of some 2,400 square kilometres (940 square miles) by 2021. This concept would be characterized by:
  ~ the lowest cost of acquiring parks and open spaces;
  ~ ready availability of serviced land, with lower risks of sudden price increases;
  ~ a more extensive road system, but increased traffic;
  ~ greater duplication of social services and facilities.
~ The *Central* concept would concentrate a great deal of growth in the central, built-up areas. It would result in an area of 1,890 square kilometres (730 square miles) and:
  ~ the least encroachment on greenlands;
  ~ a more efficient and effective transit system;
  ~ the lowest levels of air pollution and energy consumption from vehicle use;

~ the greatest opportunity to reduce pollution of rivers and lakes through upgrading of existing storm sewers;
~ better use of existing health and education facilities.
~ The *Nodal* concept would have approximately the same number of residents living outside Metropolitan Toronto in the suburban regions as in the Spread concept, but they would be grouped in compact communities, or nodes. This would result in an area of approximately 2,124 square kilometres (820 square miles) in size. This concept would lead to:
  ~ greater preservation of green space than the Spread concept but less than the Central concept;
  ~ a wider range of community sizes, housing types, densities, and population/employment patterns;
  ~ expanded crosstown rapid transit;
  ~ potential integrating of social services on a community basis.

Because the study found that, broadly speaking, the three concepts would cost roughly the same amount, the consultants concluded that the choices facing people and governments depend not so much on cost as on other factors such as environmental and economic considerations, lifestyle preferences, and the quality of community and individual life.

The Minister of Municipal Affairs, the Honourable John Sweeney, asked the municipalities of the region to consider the implications of the study for their communities and, in the next six months or so, to hold public debate and consultation on the issues.

A second initiative that may well influence this debate is the report to the provincial government on the Oak Ridges Moraine; Mr. Kanter's mandate was to make recommendations concerning the moraine, its ground and headwaters, and its river valleys. This is an important initiative and congruent with the theme articulated in the Royal

Jogging in St. Lawrence neighbourhood

Martin Goodman Trail, south of Lake Shore Boulevard

The regionalist attempts to plan such an area so that all its sites and resources, from forest to city, from highland to water level, may be soundly developed, and so that the population will be distributed so as to utilize, rather than to nullify and destroy, its natural advantages. It sees people, industry and the land as a single unit. ... Regional planning sees that the depopulated countryside and the congested city are intimately related....

Mumford, L. 1985. In *Dwellers in the land: the bioregional vision*, K. Sale. 142. San Francisco: Sierra Club.

Commission's first interim report — a clean, green, healthy waterfront demands a watershed approach, which, in turn, implies protection of headwaters and river valleys. Such a policy will obviously influence the urban form and structure of the region.

Recommendation

37. The waterfront, the Oak Ridges Moraine, and river valleys of the Greater Toronto Area should be recognized as Provincial Resources in the public debate and decisions made by all levels of government on the urban form and structure of the region.

10. Water-based Commuter Transportation

Lake Ontario itself provides an excellent opportunity for waterborne transit services connecting centres along the entire waterfront including but not limited to those from Newcastle to Burlington. Relatively high-speed services can be provided, using hovercraft or hydrofoil technology; marine transit of this type operates in many parts of the world. Direct connections across the west end of Lake Ontario could also be provided to destinations in Hamilton, Stoney Creek, and the Niagara Peninsula, and possibly to U.S. centres as well.

A private service operated a number of years ago, connecting downtown Toronto to the Niagara Peninsula, but operational difficulties eventually ended it. More recently, a private-sector proposal has been made for hovercraft service between Oshawa Harbour and downtown Toronto, a trip promoters say would take an average of forty-five minutes.

Two important questions need to be addressed in considering the feasibility of water commuter transportation:

~ Can it operate year-round, in the face of severe weather conditions and icing on Lake Ontario during winter months?

~ Is the market sufficient to make such an operation financially viable, meeting commuter, recreational, and other market needs?

If the answers to these basic questions are positive, more detailed planning and institutional assessments are required in respect of landing sites, franchises, and the role of private- and public-sector participants.

Recommendation

38. The Province of Ontario should conduct a feasibility study of all-season water-borne transit services connecting centres along the waterfront from Newcastle to Burlington, including connections to Hamilton, Stoney Creek, and centres in the Niagara Peninsula.

B. AREA-SPECIFIC ISSUES

Having considered some of the area-wide waterfront issues, the Commission now turns its attention to the way those matters affect particular geographic areas of the Greater Toronto watershed and makes recommendations specific to them.

1. Halton Region

Most of the waterfront in Halton Region is developed as single-family residential, with a relatively small component of green space. However, the Region of Halton, in its own words, "has long recognized the Lake Ontario shoreline as a finite and non-renewable resource, the significance of which transcends local municipal boundaries". That

importance can only grow to new proportions: it is projected that Halton's population will increase by 83 per cent by 2011!

Under the leadership of Halton Region, and with the co-operation of the municipalities of Oakville and Burlington and the Halton Region Conservation Authority, the Halton Region Waterfront Plan was adopted in 1982 as an amendment to the Regional Official Plan. This plan identifies regional waterfront parks as nodes of public use, with provision for recreational links. It also addresses the issue of preserving stream valleys and of formulating policies to control waterfront development. Erosion control is identified as the first priority, with land acquisition second.

The plan identifies five major projects to be developed as first-priority regional waterfront parks: Bronte Outer Harbour, Burlington Beach, Spencer Smith, Burloak and Oakville Harbour. Construction of Bronte Outer Harbour is currently under way, with the assistance of the federal Small Craft Harbours Branch, to create a marina for 450 boats. Acquisition of cottage lands and leases has been under way for a number of years on the Burlington Beach strip, although it has been severely hampered by a paucity of provincial funding assistance. The adjoining Spencer Smith Park was added to the priority list in 1989. Some land at the proposed Burloak Waterfront Park has been acquired, but high costs are limiting progress. Oakville Harbour is near completion.

In the Commission's view, the process used to develop the Halton Region Waterfront Plan is an excellent example of municipal initiative and co-ordination, and could serve as an excellent model elsewhere along the waterfront. Its preparation involved public input and extensive inter-agency co-operation. The plan spells out land acquisition, development, and other priorities for individual sites and activities; it also defines the roles of various agencies in implementation.

It is clear that the agencies involved in the Halton plan are committed to it; the

Hilton Falls, Milton

missing element in implementation has been provincial involvement. However, there are still several issues to be addressed. First, the plan, to a large extent, is recreational in emphasis, with little attention devoted to the natural features and functions of the waterfront and associated valleylands.

Second, it is worth noting that all five priority projects along the Halton waterfront involve some component of lakefill, despite the fact that the cumulative effect of both this lakefill and the extensive shore protection works needed to stop wave erosion were not fully studied. Similar shoreline modifications along the Scarborough Bluffs have already resulted in detrimental changes to the Eastern Beaches, by reducing the supply of new sand. The same potential exists here for negative effects along the sweep of Burlington Beach. Such an unforeseen result could jeopardize both the ecological stability of the beach and the investment of millions of dollars spent on developing and enhancing its recreational uses.

There is also concern that, in some places, Halton is using proposed lakefill as an easier alternative than retaining or creating public green space along the existing shore. For example, the Town of Oakville and the Region of Halton are apparently willing to allow residential development of the 4.2-hectare (10.4-acre) existing waterfront open space at the Shell House lands, while supporting the proposed 10.9 hectares (27 acres) of lakefill at Burloak Waterfront Park close by. Similarly, the City of Burlington is discussing new lakefill in its downtown east area to create public access, rather than incorporating waterfront green space into redevelopment proposals for the "motel strip" on the existing shore.

The need to weigh the comparative costs and benefits of new lakefill against those of acquiring expensive shoreline open space will likely be repeated in other places along the waterfront in coming years. It is essential that the environmental costs of lakefill are fully factored into the decision-making process.

Given the degree of uncertainty surrounding provincial lakefill policy, and its potential effect on the feasibility of future lakefilling, it is also essential that options not involving lakefill be kept in mind as much as possible.

In the Commission's view, retaining existing waterfront open space should be viewed as a priority of the first order. In line with the principle that the water's edge should be publicly accessible, programs should be put in place to acquire land as public open space where it is now used for other purposes. In Halton, the Town of Oakville currently has such a program; the City of Burlington does not.

In its presentation, the Region of Halton also asked the Commission to endorse its proposal for a Great Lakes Science Centre, to be located at the southerly end of Burlington Beach. This centre would focus on the importance of fresh water in creating a sustainable environment, and would be designed to attract visitors from local and regional areas as well as from abroad. It is intended to provide stimulating exhibits to visitors and act as a link between environmental scientists and the public. Capital costs would be shared among three levels of government, private corporations, and other donors.

Gardiner Expressway ramps

39. As requested by Halton Region, Burlington, and Oakville, the Province should declare the Halton waterfront to be of Provincial Interest under the *Planning Act*.

40. As soon as possible, the Province should negotiate a Waterfront Partnership Agreement with the Region of Halton, as well as with other levels of government and their agencies, and the private sector as appropriate. The agreement should use the existing Halton Waterfront Plan as the basis for negotiations, and should consider the following issues:

    a) a mechanism for making commitments of substantial, multi-year provincial funding to allow priority projects of the Halton Waterfront Plan (Bronte Harbour, Burlington Beach, Burloak, Oakville Harbour, Spencer Smith) to proceed;

    b) confirmation of agency roles in implementing the plan, with Halton Region as the leading co-ordinating agency;

    c) a review of the Halton Waterfront Plan's conformity to the principles of this report;

    d) expanding the ability of the Halton Region Conservation Authority to regulate shoreline and valleyland development, based on ecological and recreational objectives and on planning for protection from floods and erosion;

    e) identifying interim and preferred routes for the Waterfront Trail in Halton, as well as developing mechanisms to bring the trail into existence;

    f) making arrangements to transfer federal and provincial Crown lands and waterlots to local public agencies, at nominal cost, where they are needed for public access and use;

    g) relocating the Ministry of Transportation works yards from Burlington Beach to allow redevelopment of the present site;

    h) asking Ontario Hydro to explore the most feasible means of removing existing electrical transmission lines from Burlington Beach;

    i) completing an independent study of the cumulative effects of proposed lakefill projects and shore protection on the supply of sand to Burlington Beach and on local water quality — before including any specific approvals for further lakefill along the Halton shore in the agreement;

    j) identifying opportunities and plans to maintain or create green corridors up the valleys of Grindstone Creek, Bronte Creek, and Sixteen Mile Creek, and to preserve and enhance natural habitats at other creek mouths such as Fourteen Mile Creek and Shoreacres Creek;

    k) a review of the City of Burlington's current policy of not requiring that the water's edge be dedicated for public use as part of redevelopment activities;

    l) assessing opportunities for creating waterfront green space without the use of extensive lakefill in the Burlington Downtown East area;

    m) re-examining the designation of the waterfront Shell House lands and the design of the proposed Burloak lakefill park, in the context of the population increases projected in the *Draft Shell Lands Secondary Plan*, to determine the feasibility of obtaining the Shell House lands as public open space;

    n) financial arrangements under which the federal and provincial governments, and the private sector, would participate in the development of the proposed Great Lakes Science Centre, as a means of communicating the historical, environmental, recreational, and economic importance of Great Lakes rehabilitation to the public.

2. City of Mississauga

The Mississauga waterfront has a varied mix of uses and ownership, and includes several major utilities. While some 56 per cent of the shoreline is now in public hands, only 33 per cent of the waterfront is publicly accessible. With a rapidly expanding population and increasing demands for waterfront recreation, Mississauga has shown great interest in its waterfront in recent years.

The Mississauga waterfront was included in the 1967 Waterfront Plan for the Metropolitan Toronto Planning Area, and in 1971 the Credit Valley Conservation Authority (CVCA) was designated by the Province as the implementing agency. Since then, the CVCA has undertaken major lakefill projects at J.C. Saddington Park and at Lakefront Promenade Park, and is scheduled to relocate the Port Credit Yacht Club to the latter site next year.

In 1987, the City of Mississauga endorsed the *Port Credit Harbour and Waterfront Concept* report, which recommended redevelopment and expansion of J.C. Saddington Park to incorporate the Canadian Sport Fishing Hall of Fame and harbours for transient and seasonal docking. It also recommended a major redevelopment of both sides of the Credit River below Lake Shore Road, to create a commercial and public activity centre to be called Harbour Square.

These proposals have not yet been implemented, largely because of a lack of funding, and because of the difficulty of providing the long-term tenure needed by private investors on the Harbour Square lands, which are owned by the federal government. The *Land Management Study for the Port Credit Harbour Area*, commissioned by the City and completed in December 1989, proposes that the federal lands in question be turned over to the City to facilitate arrangements for private investment.

The City of Mississauga has also initiated preparation of a waterfront plan along the entire waterfront, with a 30-year planning horizon. The documents *Fundamentals, Vision 2020*, and *Implementation* were released for public review in June 1990. The waterfront plan is scheduled to be completed in early 1991.

While the Commission has not yet been able to review these documents in detail, their general orientation appears consistent with many of the principles outlined in this report. The Mississauga waterfront presents a number of significant opportunities for progress in the short term, particularly with respect to industrial sites that are coming available for redevelopment. The Commission is confident that the City of Mississauga, given an appropriate level of support and assistance from other agencies, will take advantage of these opportunities and treat the future of its waterfront with competence, vigour, and sensitivity.

Exploring along the Humber River

Recommendations

41. As requested by the City of Mississauga, the Province should recognize the Mississauga waterfront as a Provincial Resource, and declare the area to be of Provincial Interest under the *Planning Act*.

42. As part of the approval process for the Mississauga Waterfront Plan, the Province should negotiate a Waterfront Partnership Agreement with the City of Mississauga, the Credit Valley Conservation Authority, the federal government, and other appropriate agencies and private-sector interests. This agreement should be largely based on the waterfront plan currently in preparation and on the Port Credit Harbour master plan, and should include consideration of, among other things:

   a) providing substantial, multi-year provincial funding to allow priority projects to proceed;

   b) designating the roles of various agencies in implementing such an agreement, with the City of Mississauga in the lead co-ordinating role;

   c) a review of the conformity of the plans to the principles of this report;

   d) incorporating the results of the approved Mississauga waterfront plan into the official plan and secondary plans, with the power to override existing zoning;

   e) expanding the ability of the Credit Valley Conservation Authority to regulate shoreline and valleyland development, based on ecological and recreational objectives, as well as to protect against floods and erosion;

   f) transferring ownership of the Ontario Hydro waterfront property at the mouth of Joshua Creek to the City of Mississauga;

   g) designating preferred and interim routes for the Waterfront Trail, including a requirement that both Ontario Hydro and the provincial agency responsible for water and sewer facilities negotiate public walkways and bicycle paths across their properties;

   h) developing strategies to maintain or create green corridors up the Credit River and Etobicoke Creek, and to enhance other existing or potential wildlife and fisheries habitats along the shore;

   i) establishing suitable mechanisms to permit redevelopment of the Port Credit Harbour, preferably by transfer of federal lands to the City or some other appropriate means;

   j) transferring the Canadian Arsenals property from Canada Post Corporation to an appropriate conservation agency, by means of a land exchange so it can be managed as part of Marie Curtis Park.

A diversified port that is dependent on many sources of revenue and subject to a wide range of environmental and land use requirements can no longer afford to proceed on an ad-hoc, project-by-project basis. Long-term planning is no longer a luxury but a necessity.

Hershman, M. J. 1988. "Harbor management: a new role for the public port." In *Urban ports and harbor management: responding to change along U.S. waterfronts*, editor M. J. Hershman. 19. New York: Taylor & Francis.

3. City of Etobicoke

The City of Etobicoke's waterfront faces crucial choices for the future. It has been said that there is no area in the GTA that will experience as much change in the next ten years as south Etobicoke. The waterfront area, generally south of the CNR tracks, has recently been the subject of intense pressures that are now converging and gaining momentum. Among the issues confronting the area are high-density water's-edge development, public access, de-industrialization and concomitant high-density development, water quality, lakefill, and the adequacy of the transportation infrastructure and of community services.

In a very real sense, the Etobicoke waterfront is a microcosm of the issues, problems, and opportunities along the broader GTA waterfront.

Changing values, such as the upsurge in environmental consciousness and the concern about the quality of life in an intensely urbanized setting, appear to have caught decision-makers unaware. It is not that the City is without plans but, rather, that the plans to which it has committed itself, and those it is contemplating, may not have been formulated on the basis of an integrated and comprehensive approach. Public concerns about the barrier effect of high-density development at the water's edge, about waterfront access and the cumulative impact of lake-filling, have not yet been fully resolved. Instead, decision-makers in the City have been quick to support development applications and to grant high densities, because they view the waterfront area as stagnating and in need of revitalization.

Between 1981 and 1986, the Etobicoke waterfront community had a stable population of about 40,000 residents and little new development. However, in the three years 1987, 1988, and 1989, almost 1,500 residential units were started, close to 90 per cent of them exclusive water's-edge condominiums. Public concern about the privatization of the waterfront and the barrier effect of high-density development has galvanized opposition to major redevelopment proposals.

WATERFRONT PLANNING

For the most part, waterfront planning in Etobicoke has been done on the basis of site-specific development applications and narrow area-specific secondary plans. In essence, this type of planning has reacted to, and been led by, development applications, rather than providing a context in which public values and objectives are sought and applied. In the process, the waterfront has been viewed as an adjunct to — rather than an integral part of — Etobicoke's broader community. Instead of seeing the waterfront and river valleys as the natural context within which comprehensive planning should take place, these have been treated largely as constraints to development — to be modified, adjusted, and overcome.

Etobicoke's existing Official Plan and its proposed Official Plan Update do not treat the waterfront as an area requiring a special planning strategy. Instead, the land-water interface and adjoining developments are subject to the same general planning strategy as other areas in the urban structure. The only exception is that part of the Official Plan Update concerned with environmental protection and development constraints. However, even this section provides only limited strategic guidance concerning waterfront environmental issues.

Normally, secondary plans are built on the policies and strategies found in official plans. However, in the absence of a clear planning strategy for the entire Etobicoke waterfront, both secondary plans and site-specific applications are made in the face of a lack of clear strategic guidance and public objectives. This lack of clear direction is of particular concern, given the very high densities permitted or proposed for major sections of the Etobicoke waterfront. The Motel Strip Secondary Plan is perhaps the most glaring example of this reactive approach.

THE MOTEL STRIP SECONDARY PLAN

The Motel Strip Secondary Plan (approved by Etobicoke Council in February 1988 and revised in May 1990) is the only secondary plan approved by Council for any portion of the Etobicoke waterfront. A secondary plan for the area west of Islington Avenue has recently been initiated in response to three major development applications. However, it focuses specifically on development sites, rather than on the waterfront area. (A study of the Mimico area was completed in 1983 but is still under review by Council.)

The basis for the Motel Strip Secondary Plan is a 1977 provincial Cabinet decision concerning comprehensive assembly of the 16.2-hectare (40-acre) S. B. McLaughlin lands. That decision provided for 2,700 dwelling units on 16.2 hectares (40 acres) of land and water — a gross density of 167 units per hectare (68 units per acre). In effect, density was assigned to both the land (13.2 hectares, or 32.5 acres) and water (3.0 hectares, or 7.5 acres) components of the site. However, for all practical purposes, only the density assigned to the land could be built — since developing the water component depended on a multitude of approvals that lay beyond individual developer and municipal control.

However, the proposed Secondary Plan, approved by Etobicoke Council in 1988, took the 1977 Cabinet decision one step further, by providing for density to be transferred from the water portion to the land portion of the site. The result of the density transfer from the water portion of the site is that the developers can build as much as 35 per cent more than would otherwise be permitted on just the land portion. The resulting net density on the developable land area (excluding water, a school, and parks) is 316 units per hectare (128 units per acre), or roughly equivalent to that of the adjacent 45-storey Palace Pier development.

Because of the very high residential densities, even higher densities were considered necessary to encourage commercial and mixed-use development. The plan accomplished this by providing for a maximum net density of 3.5 times lot area for residential projects but 4.0 times lot area (almost 15 per cent higher) for commercial and mixed-use projects. All areas within the plan were then designated either commercial or mixed-use at the higher maximum density.

Added to these very high, and increasing, densities were potential density bonuses and the treatment of any senior citizens' unit built as equalling one-third of a regular unit, although there was no limit on the size of a seniors' unit.

The Motel Strip Secondary Plan was revised in May 1990, in part to reflect the results of a provincially initiated Environmental Management Master Plan/Public Amenity Scheme for the area (discussed later in more detail). However, in advance of this revised secondary plan, Etobicoke Council granted conditional approval to three development applications for the motel strip, the most recent on 30 April 1990, at a net density, with bonuses, of 4.8 times lot area. The three approved applications, covering 6.1 hectares (15 acres), or 30 per cent of the area, represent more than 1,200 units and allow maximum building heights of 26 to 29 storeys. The approved applications also raise the number of "committed" units in the motel strip to 2,666 — 34 units short of the maximum.

The Revised Secondary Plan no longer requires comprehensive assembly of the 16.2-hectare (40-acre) McLaughlin portion as a condition for developing the 2,700 units. This change is rationalized on the very narrow basis of traffic capacity, apparently without analysing the impact of all development applications outside the area or considering the waterfront location.

The proposed waterfront public amenity strip in the revised plan was widened from the initial minimum width of 15 metres (50 feet) to a width of from 50 to 80 metres (160 to 260 feet), predominantly by the proposed use of shoreline lakefill. Furthermore, the revised plan permits incremental development of the waterfront public amenity area — precisely the approach to providing parks and open space that was taken by Harbourfront Corporation.

The revised plan also allows reduced parkland dedication to be considered, as well as off-site development of the affordable housing component and a school site to be designated only if the form and occupancy of development warrants it. The overall effect is to maximize the mass of buildings, encourage adult lifestyles (offsetting the requirement for a school), and front-end load the residential development on a small land base.

The Commission considers that, within the overall context of its waterfront location, building heights and densities for the motel strip are too high. It does not deem the Palace Pier development to the east, and the Marina Del Ray/Grand Harbour developments to the west, to be appropriate benchmarks for the motel strip. What is being proposed for the area is not consistent with public values, the ecosystem approach, and the principles articulated in this report. The need for visual and physical access to the waterfront, as well as for public use of it, point to the necessity of modifying the plan.

The Ontario Municipal Board is to begin hearings on the Motel Strip Secondary Plan on 19 November 1990. Part of the focus will be on the Environmental Management Master Plan for the motel strip.

Environmental Management Master Plan

Citizens' concerns about the density of proposed development in the motel strip and about proposed lakefilling led to a request, in August 1988, that the Motel Strip Secondary Plan area be designated under the *Environmental Assessment Act*. The matter was first referred to the Ontario Environmental Assessment Advisory Committee, which recommended that privately held land on the motel strip not be subject to the *Environmental Assessment Act*, but that shoreline and nearshore redevelopment be submitted to it. The committee further recommended that the Province take an active co-ordinating role, to ensure that cumulative environmental and planning effects were fully considered.

In the end, it was decided not to subject any part of the redevelopment to review under the *Environmental Assessment Act*. Instead, the Province declared a Provincial Interest in the motel strip and began an Environmental Management Master Plan/Public Amenity Scheme process within the context of the *Planning Act*. This process was intended to bridge the gap between environmental and planning concerns.

Among the broader environmental issues affecting the motel strip are water quality and contaminated sediments. The strip is located on the western shore of Humber Bay, between the Humber River and Mimico Creek. The entire bay has been identified by the International Joint Commission as a Great Lakes Area of Concern because of contaminants in the aquatic sediments, metals and organics in the water and biota, and elevated levels of nutrients and bacterial contaminants. Water quality is generally poor because of pollution from the Humber River, Mimico Creek, and the Humber Sewage Treatment Plant.

The bay is sheltered from the main-lake circulation currents and has been described as a "bathymetric trap", in which most of the sediment discharged into it accumulates and remains relatively undisturbed. An area of sediment, described by the Ministry of the Environment as "highly contaminated", extends south of the motel strip and as much as three kilometres into the bay.

One deputant at the Royal Commission's environment and health hearings in May 1990 stated that the Environmental Management Master Plan (EMMP) for the motel strip was "an unknown quantity" when it was initially proposed, because one had never been undertaken before. The EMMP was subsequently completed in September 1989 and formed part of the basis for revisions to the Motel Strip Secondary Plan.

In submissions to the Commission, deputants commented on some of the shortcomings of the EMMP process, among them:

~ The study was undertaken over a short period (three months), which did not allow the consultants to hear adequately from the community.
~ The consultants were not directed to question density and land use on the motel strip and, consequently, most of their emphasis was on the treatment of the water's edge.
~ There were no new data collected that would have added to the body of existing knowledge of the environmental impact and other concerns about the area.
~ The consultants' first major recommendation was that a deflector arm be used to reduce resuspension of contaminated sediments and deflect pollution from the Humber Sewage Treatment Plant. However, there was no study of the best way to deal with the contaminated sediments or any indication of the intended place to which the pollution from the treatment plant would be deflected.

One deputant cited these as examples of the problems of addressing environmental matters in the context of the *Planning Act*, and noted that, "under the *Planning Act* there is no clear-cut process and there is no requirement to look at alternatives, either to the undertakings or to the solutions and the recommendations."

~ The consultants' second major environmental recommendation was to create marshes as a filter for stormwater from the motel strip. A deputant at an environmental hearing of the Royal Commission asked,

What is going to be the impact of the filling required to create the wetlands in the first place, on the contaminated sediments that we know exist in the embayment?

And if 6.5 hectares (16 acres) of wetlands do not grow there, and it does not work, and we have built all of the high-rises on the motel strip without providing any other kind of environmentally acceptable stormwater drainage schemes, what do we do then?

~ Because environmental matters on the motel strip are being dealt with under the *Planning Act*, and will eventually be heard before the Ontario Municipal Board (OMB), citizens are not eligible for the Intervenor Funding that would have been available had the issues been handled under the *Environmental Assessment Act*.

These criticisms show the flaws in the current EMMP process. However, the process was begun only after the initial Motel Strip Secondary Plan had been formulated; moreover, the OMB hearing and any

There is not an acre of land anywhere in the world that is not loved by someone.

Stefansson, V. c. 1930 (Attributed).

Port of Toronto salt storage, MT 51

subsequent Cabinet review of the OMB decision have not yet occurred.

Nevertheless, especially in light of the experience over the past year, there is every indication of a need to work out a process that merges environmental and planning considerations; furthermore, the Province should address the issue of Intervenor Funding at the earliest possible time.

The concerns expressed by people appearing before the Commission simply reinforce the recommendations contained on pages 180 to 186 of its 1989 interim report: the *Planning Act* should be amended to ensure that environmental concerns are more thoroughly identified and addressed as part of the planning process.

The Minister of the Environment has stated that the proposed deflector arm will be subject to a separate environmental assessment. The deflector arm represents 5.1 hectares (12.6 acres) of lakefill, the other lakefill components being a shoreline smoothing/ public amenity strip of 3.7 hectares (9.1 acres) and the creation of marshes/stormwater management of 6.5 hectares (16 acres).

In essence, the lakefill proposals contained in the EMMP have become incrementalized. While the shoreline smoothing may make some sense in encouraging flushing action along the shore, the deflector arm has the potential to reduce flushing and create a relatively stagnant embayment. Perhaps not surprisingly, the deflector arm, while recognized as being subject to a separate environmental assessment, is included in the revised Motel Strip Secondary Plan. Although the EMMP process has assisted in clarifying the nature of the public amenity area in the motel strip, it is neither a comprehensive approach to lakefill concerns or environmental matters in the area covered by the secondary plan nor an adequate response to urban design and density considerations.

DE-INDUSTRIALIZATION AND HIGH-DENSITY DEVELOPMENT

De-industrialization has become a significant issue in the broader context of the waterfront area and its immediate hinterland. Between 1983 and 1989, industrial employment in the Etobicoke waterfront area fell by 32 per cent, as 2,234 full-time industrial jobs were lost and 65 part-time industrial jobs created. The decline was even more dramatic between 1985 and 1989, when industrial employment peaked. In 1985 there were 7,405 industrial jobs in the Etobicoke waterfront area — 7,332 full-time and 73 part-time. However, by 1989, there were only 4,691 industrial jobs, of which 4,592 were full-time and 99 part-time — an overall decline between 1985 and 1989 of 37 per cent.

Taking all employment categories into account, between 1983 and 1989 the Etobicoke waterfront area experienced a marginal increase in overall employment of 196 jobs, roughly two-per-cent growth. However, this was accomplished through the net loss of 652 full-time jobs (representing a six-per-cent loss) and a gain of 848 part-time jobs (a 98-per-cent increase). In effect, the significant loss of well-paying, full-time industrial jobs was offset by increases in service-sector employment, predominantly office and institutional, where growth of part-time jobs was strongest.

Among the industries that have closed, or are in the process of doing so, those in the waterfront area include the Goodyear Tire plant, Pittsburgh Paints, Arrowhead Metals, Neptune Meters, and numerous smaller plants; and, a little further to the north, McGuinness Distillers, Federal Nut and Bolt, Sunbeam Corporation, and Noxzema.

The municipality has already approved rezoning of the Goodyear site (8.1 hectares, or 20 acres) to residential, and the McGuinness site (6.2 hectares, or 15.4 acres) and the Long Branch Village lands (11.7 hectares, or 28.8 acres) are currently in the development review process. It is likely that rezoning of these industrial lands will put pressure on remaining industry in the area, because of a substantial increase in land value resulting from zoning changes to high-density residential use. Thereby, perhaps somewhat inadvertently, the municipality has set the stage for further de-industrialization.

Together, the three current industrial rezonings involve 26 hectares (64.2 acres) with development applications for 7,134 dwelling units and a gross residential density of 274 units per hectare (109 units per acre). In addition, they include more than 116,100 square metres (1,250,000 square feet) predominantly for office and retail use, and maximum building heights of 35, 28, and 15 storeys. It is proposed that net densities on the various sites will range from 4.2 to 5.1 times lot area, or more than those of the motel strip.

For comparative purposes, the net densities that have been approved or applied for are well in excess of net densities for St. James Town, the St. Lawrence Neighbourhood, and Harbourfront — all of which are at 3.0 times lot area.

Taking into account the motel strip and all current development applications related to the Etobicoke waterfront, the cumulative effect could be the construction of almost 12,000 dwelling units and 251,000 square metres (2,700,000 square feet) of non-residential space in the waterfront area. Additional development applications for former industrial sites north of the CNR tracks are expected to add further to this total. One estimate places the potential population increase in south Etobicoke at between 25,000 and 37,000 persons by 2006.

CUMULATIVE IMPACT

Concern about the cumulative impact of development in Etobicoke has been growing. In April 1990 Metropolitan Toronto Council, acting on the recommendation of its commissioner of planning, asked the City of Etobicoke to prepare an overview report for their lakeshore area. The report is intended to provide a broader context for assessing the policy implications of planning decisions on individual sites. Metropolitan Toronto defined its primary concerns in the Etobicoke lakeshore area as being:

~ affordable housing;
~ the economy (i.e., the continuing viability of industrial lands);

~ providing Metropolitan Toronto services and infrastructure;

~ environmental protection;

~ public access to the waterfront.

At the same time, the Honourable John Sweeney, Minister of Municipal Affairs and Housing, expressed his concern about the need for comprehensive planning in south Etobicoke. In a letter written to Etobicoke Mayor Bruce Sinclair, Mr. Sweeney proposed that:

> a comprehensive overview of the broader implications of redevelopment in south Etobicoke be undertaken by the City in consultation with the Province and Metropolitan Toronto. It should deal with the overall impact, including costs, of development on infrastructure as well as community facilities and services in this area ... and ... recommendations emanating from this study [should] be incorporated into the Official Plan by way of modification.

Because of the dramatic de-industrialization in the area of Etobicoke south of Bloor Street, it is likely, in the next several years, to be the place with the most intense pressures for change in all of the GTA. Such a scale of change creates problems but also offers great opportunity. Coping will require comprehensive planning and co-operation among the Province, Metropolitan Toronto, and Etobicoke. If the area's potential is to be realized, all levels of government will have to work and plan together. Until this co-operation is secured, it is necessary to pause and allow for thorough strategic planning.

Recommendations

43. The Province should declare the Etobicoke waterfront area and its immediate hinterland an area of Provincial Interest under the *Planning Act*.

44. The Province, Metropolitan Toronto, and Etobicoke should jointly undertake strategic planning for the Etobicoke waterfront area and its immediate hinterland, culminating in a comprehensive Etobicoke Waterfront Plan and a consolidated waterfront component for the Official Plan. Such planning in Etobicoke should be co-ordinated with work Metropolitan Toronto is currently undertaking on a new Metropolitan Toronto Waterfront Plan. Among the issues to be addressed and integrated into the Etobicoke planning studies are:

    a) building heights and densities;

    b) urban design guidelines for the waterfront;

    c) affordable housing;

    d) de-industrialization;

    e) provision of community services, transportation, and infrastructure;

    f) environmental protection;

    g) public access and public open spaces;

    h) full and appropriate public participation;

    i) secondary plans and amendments to secondary plans in the waterfront area;

    j) overview studies of the waterfront area recommended by Metropolitan Toronto.

45. In order to protect the integrity of the study while it is being done, the Province should utilize the appropriate section of the *Planning Act* to impose a moratorium on development in the Etobicoke waterfront area and its immediate hinterland. Such a moratorium should remain in effect until a comprehensive Waterfront Plan for the area and an updated Official Plan, which conform to the ecosystem approach and principles outlined in this report, are adopted.

4. Toronto's Central Waterfront

Adjacent to and integrated with the downtown, Toronto's Central Waterfront is the core of Canada's biggest financial and economic powerhouse. It includes the Railway Lands and Ataratiri, two of Canada's largest downtown redevelopment projects; significant natural areas such as the Leslie Street Spit and Tommy Thompson Park; and such major tourist, cultural, and recreational amenities as Exhibition Place and Ontario Place, Fort York, the Toronto Islands, Harbourfront, the CN Tower, and SkyDome. Its major transportation facilities include Union Station, the rail corridor, the Gardiner/Lake Shore arterial road system, the Port of Toronto, and the Toronto Island Airport, as well as subway, bus, and train lines. It also contains major commercial and industrial installations, and power and wastewater plants.

plans for the area are being renewed and updated, and the Office of the Greater Toronto Area is exploring new urban strategies.

At the same time, the waterfront is also the area in the region under the greatest ecological stress. All of this provides a unique opportunity to adopt the ecosystem approach and apply ecosystem principles. One or more Waterfront Partnership Agreements could be considered for the Central Waterfront, but work is required first.

ACCESS AND TRANSPORTATION IN THE CENTRAL WATERFRONT

The central fact of the Central Waterfront is the existence of the Gardiner/Lake Shore Corridor. Depending on the decision made about its future, the people of Greater Toronto will have an excellent waterfront — or they will not. The waterfront will be integrated into downtown Toronto — or it will remain essentially separate from it.

Harbourfront LRT opening, June 1990

The whole of this area is undergoing dynamic evolution and change: the East Bayfront, Port Industrial Area, Railway Lands, Greenwood Racetrack, Harbourfront, Exhibition Place, and Canada Post lands at 40 Bay Street — all are in a state of transition. Large privately owned parcels in the area, such as Molson's, Dylex, and Loblaws, are going to be redeveloped. City and Metro

The choices made for the Gardiner/Lake Shore Corridor will have a fundamental impact on the shape, scope, and potential of the financial district, Exhibition Place, Ontario Place, Fort York, Harbourfront, the Railway Lands, Ataratiri, East Bayfront, the Port Industrial Area, and South Riverdale.

The combination of the elevated portion of the Gardiner Expressway, Lake Shore Boulevard underneath it, and the rail corridor beside it, has created a physical, visual,

End of shift, Port of Toronto

Summertime cruising, Toronto Islands

and psychological barrier to the Central Waterfront. It is a constant source of noise and air pollution, a hostile, dirty environment for thousands of people who walk under it daily, and a barrier to thousands of others who risk life and limb to get across or around it. The Gardiner/Lake Shore is not only a road: it is a structure. As it processes traffic, it stunts land use; meant to move us along, it limits our opportunities.

At its public hearings, the Commission heard many proposals regarding the future of the elevated portion of the expressway, details of which are available from the Commission. However, stated briefly, they comprise three options:

~ Leave it in place and reduce the barrier effect by improving lighting, tree-planting, beautification works, and urban design.
~ Dismantle it and provide sufficient transportation capacity by enhancing arterial roads and improving public transit.
~ Build an expressway tunnel under or adjacent to Lake Shore Boulevard or

along the existing shoreline and only then take down the elevated expressway.

In addition to the information obtained from its public hearings, the Commission embarked on a series of meetings and discussions with a number of groups, individuals, and interested parties to elicit further opinions and suggestions about the Gardiner/Lake Shore. Finally, in June, it called together some 30 people from government agencies and special-purpose bodies, as well as interested private-sector experts, including engineers, planners, and architects.

From all of this, the Royal Commission has concluded that the elevated portion of the Gardiner-Lake Shore Expressway is incompatible with the fundamental environmental and land-use objectives in the Central Waterfront. Metro's present annual capital maintenance program for the expressway is enough to maintain the current structure for approximately 20 years — which presents both a practical opportunity and a compelling necessity to dismantle the elevated expressway in that time.

The Commission feels that, in general, the second option described above would be the best approach, and that a phased development and implementation program could be put into place, integrating plans for taking down the expressway with those for improved transportation services. Such a program would deal with needed enhancement of public transit, roadways, pedestrian walkways, and bicycle paths in the area. It could also include many of the other helpful suggestions made by the Gardiner/Lake Shore Task Force, on improvements to urban design, as suggested in the *Lower Yonge Street Study*. The Commission also notes the Task Force's many useful recommendations for land-use and roadway improvements that could be made in the Lower Don if the elevated Gardiner were removed and Lake Shore Boulevard re-aligned.

Recommendations

46. The elevated section of the Gardiner-Lake Shore Expressway should be taken down, in a phased program, over the next 20 years.

47. As part of the process, plans should be made to improve public transit, roadway, pedestrian, and bicycle transportation. Such transportation improvement plans should:
    a) emphasize east and west extensions of the Harbourfront LRT, closely integrated with other TTC routes and connected to new or relocated "shoulder" stations on GO Transit's Lake Shore Line;
    b) ensure that better north-south pedestrian links and bicycle connections are made and maintained. Emphasis should be placed on new pedestrian and bicycle connections passing over the rail corridor, pedestrian plazas, and improved intersection design and crossings at Lake Shore Boulevard and related roads;
    c) include revitalization of the Martin Goodman Trail, as part of the Waterfront Trail, particularly the central section between Cherry Street and Stadium Road, including pathways under the rail corridor and under the elevated section of the Gardiner existing at the time.

48. The integrated dismantling/transportation plan should be available for consideration by the City, Metropolitan Toronto, and the Province by 31 May 1991. The Commission has included this in its fall 1990 work plan.

As it crosses over major north-south arteries such as York, Bay, and Yonge streets, the rail corridor is a major barrier between the City and the waterfront, visually and in day-to-day pedestrian use. The effect can be greatly reduced by such changes as glass partitions between the sidewalk and road traffic, improved lighting, and possibly opening up retail outlets along the sidewalks under the rail corridor.

The length of the underpass and its barrier effect will be substantially reduced when the rail corridor is narrowed in preparation for redeveloping the Railway Lands.

Pedestrian walkways and amenities could be greatly improved south of the railway corridor, as suggested by the Gardiner/Lake Shore Task Force, which proposed tree-lined, widened sidewalks and improved pedestrian crossings to recreate Lower Yonge as an urban street, rather than an expressway ramp.

Another promising possibility would be to deck over the rail corridor in the central area, to allow pedestrian access between the City and the waterfront, in conjunction with a newly created plaza and park, which would have harbour vistas.

EXHIBITION PLACE, ONTARIO PLACE, FORT YORK, HMCS YORK, AND NEIGHBOURING LANDS

Among them, Exhibition Place, Ontario Place, Fort York, HMCS York, and neighbouring public lands encompass more than 200 hectares (500 acres). After the Toronto Islands, they form the largest single body of public recreational land across the entire Greater Toronto Waterfront.

They are a magnificent resource, but one that, at present, is only partially used and just occasionally of benefit to the public at large. The sites and adjacent lands have reached critical points in their history, and major decisions about their future direction are imminent. An opportunity exists to take full advantage of their extraordinary location to offer a waterfront experience for all Torontonians, unique to Toronto and a remarkable showplace for the world.

In this part of the Cental Waterfront, there are also large sites in the private sector,

now being considered for new uses, which should be incorporated into any overall plan for the area.

Over the years, numerous task forces and reports have suggested new master plans to make more productive use of Exhibition Place and overcome the sense of isolation and faded glory that characterizes the grounds so much of the time. Such a strategy is needed more now because of the loss of major sporting and entertainment events to the SkyDome. While reviewing the site's long-term future, Metropolitan Toronto has been renovating facilities at the west end of Exhibition Place, including the Ontario Government and Music buildings. Existing exhibition facilities, which are limited, are used to capacity and make money on an operating basis. However, the site as a whole waits for a stronger definition of its future.

Ontario Place is at a similar, though less obvious, decision point. Its grounds and buildings are well maintained and substantial new capital has been invested recently to upgrade its entertainment facilities. However, Ontario Place has a sizeable annual operating loss. Its competitive position in the context of other regional entertainment facilities is weak and major capital investment will be required to enable it to find a place in the leisure market.

With few exceptions, the Ontario Place grounds are open only for the summer season, limiting public accessibility to this waterfront resource. Its predominant market base is also limited, serving primarily the young and boat-owners.

Fort York is one of Toronto's most venerable historic assets. The site, however, is visually and physically inaccessible — almost totally cut off by transportation lines and overwhelmed by the elevated Gardiner. The handsome Fort York Armoury is seldom used by the general public and its adjacent lot is occupied by aging army trucks.

A new master plan is being developed by the Toronto Historical Board to overcome these problems. In searching for a broader sense of what public interest the site can serve, new uses have to take into account the fort's special historical significance, the place the grounds have in Canadian history and, in particular, their importance to the people of Toronto.

HMCS York — a naval reserve training establishment leased by the Department of National Defence from the City of Toronto — occupies a prominent, strategic waterfront location between Harbourfront and Stadium Road to the east and Coronation Park to the west. Unfortunately, public access is not permitted on or through this publicly owned property, which means that, at this point, a continuous waterfront public trail system would not be at the water's edge.

Proposals have been made to redevelop the Molson's site and adjacent lands, formerly used for industrial purposes, which could offer the opportunity to open up the Fort York site and connect it with the City and the waterfront. There are also interesting possibilities for linking these open spaces as far north as Trinity Bellwoods Park.

Coronation Park — which, with its mature stands of trees, is one of the loveliest of Toronto's waterfront parks — is little used because of its relative inaccessibility. No waterfront pedestrian route connects to the east or west because of the restrictions, respectively, of HMCS York and Ontario Place. Lake Shore Boulevard limits easy access from the north and the park is not well served by public transit. Gore Park, a potentially important link between Coronation Park and Fort York, suffers from its use as temporary parking.

Clearly, although they differ from each other, these sites suffer from similar problems:

~ locations that are isolated from the City;
~ inadequate public transportation;
~ confused or obscure public images;
~ sites used primarily in summer;
~ limited utilization;
~ heavy demands on the public sector for operating funds;

~ income inadequate to fund required capital improvements;
~ a need for investment in new facilities;
~ uncertainty about the role and extent of private investment;
~ jurisdictional conflict and confusion;
~ lack of a clear long-term master plan for the future.

These problems have solutions, but they cannot be achieved if each public authority operates in isolation or with indifference to the needs and dreams of others. Obviously, a collaborative approach is essential.

The Royal Commission has already begun such an approach and is convinced that the will exists among the authorities to develop an overall, long-term, integrated plan for these sites and lands based on the following considerations:

~ First, there is a need to overcome the area's isolation, in order to develop connections between it and the rest of the City. There are opportunities to link Coronation Park, Gore Park, and Fort York as far as Trinity Bellwoods Park, and to take advantage of proposed transportation changes, such as removing the elevated section of the Gardiner, covering Lake Shore Boulevard, and extending The Esplanade and Queen's Quay westward, in order to tie the City to this important part of its western lakefront.

The City of Toronto is growing towards these lands — witness the King Business Centre, the wave of renovation of old industrial buildings north of Exhibition Place, and the potential redevelopment of the Molson's and adjacent lands. One way to overcome the present isolation of the area is to open it up to greater public use by extending a network of public "park streets" through it — like those in New York's Central Park or London's Hyde Park, which provide vehicular access at off-peak

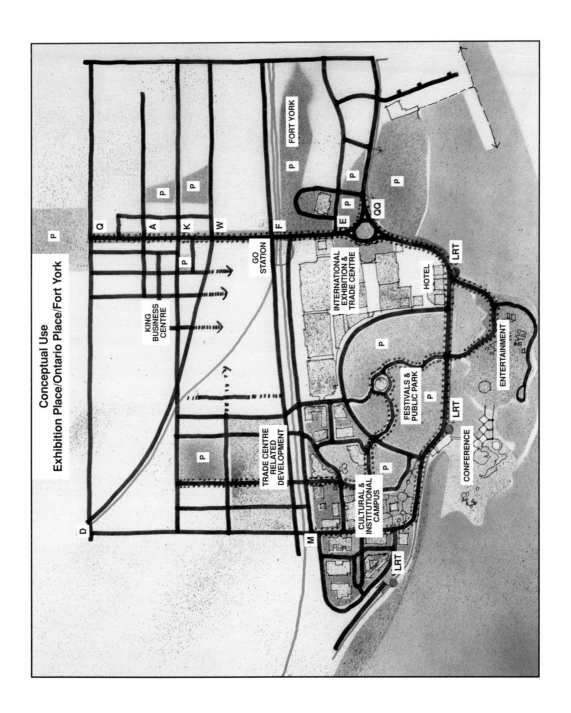

Conceptual Use
Exhibition Place/Ontario Place/Fort York

FORT YORK

GO STATION

KING BUSINESS CENTRE

INTERNATIONAL EXHIBITION & TRADE CENTRE

HOTEL

TRADE CENTRE RELATED DEVELOPMENT

FESTIVALS & PUBLIC PARK

CULTURAL & INSTITUTIONAL CAMPUS

ENTERTAINMENT

CONFERENCE

LRT

125

times and are closed at times of high park use.

Among other possibilities consistent with the principle of relieving isolation in the area: bringing Queen's Quay to the Princes' Gate and running it through Exhibition Place, along the water's edge, over or beside a covered Lake Shore Boulevard, and connecting it to Dufferin Street to provide access to the centre of the grounds; or establishing a crescent of streets to serve the proposed trade centre and the west end, linking back across the tracks to Parkdale.

In keeping with the Commission's belief that it is essential to link the City and the waterfront, Strachan Avenue could be redesigned to become a handsome street connecting the north to the lake.

Relieving isolation also has implications for public transit; in the case of the Exhibition Place area, that means extending the LRT to and through the site, with appropriate stops along the way. It is also important to relocate the GO Transit station so that it can serve both the Lake Shore West and Georgetown/ Milton lines, and link with Lester B. Pearson International Airport — a great benefit for recreational and business activities in the area.

Finally, it must be recognized that the treatment of the Lake Shore Boulevard barrier is a critical element in integrating the lands and making the best possible use of this section of the waterfront.

~ Second, the master plan must be based on the principle of redeploying and modernizing the entertainment functions of Ontario Place and Exhibition Place; the two facilities offer major entertainment attractions, but of very different types and durations, organized in very different ways.

The proposed new international trade centre and the possibility of a new Olympic Stadium would displace much of the existing CNE midway, thereby creating an opportunity to move, modernize, and consolidate the midway at the southern end adjacent to Ontario Place, and would give the combined location a critical mass of activity, thereby making it more attractive and competitive.

The grounds should also be the site of a series of large festivals, to be staged as early as possible in the spring, through to Canada Day, the CHIN Picnic, and right to the end of an extended CNE. At the same time, the potential for a winter festival should be explored.

~ The third consideration is that the park-like character of the area must be maintained and public access to it must be extended. The grounds at both Ontario Place and Exhibition Place could be landscaped and be publicly accessible year-round, in the manner of Copenhagen's justly famous Tivoli Gardens, rather than being a pay-to-enter park. By attracting an increased number of visitors, the area would be able to support activities year-round and should provide a more secure economic base for operations.

The Waterfront Trail should pass through the area, connecting to the Martin Goodman Trail, as well as to a network of walking, jogging, bicycling, and cross-country ski trails. The use of the grounds for equestrian activities should be developed more comprehensively and publicly, as part of a greater emphasis on both commercial and recreational sports. This area lends itself well to more active pursuits, in contrast to passive activities, like bird-watching, that are popular at such sites as the Leslie Street Spit.

~ Fourth, principles of heritage protection and rehabilitation must be applied in order to ensure continuity and an historic sense of place. The Princes' Gates, Old Fort York, the Automotive and Music buildings, the trees in Centennial

Park — all have been historical reference points for Torontonians for decades, and should be respected, protected, and enhanced as such.

Finding appropriate permanent uses for the public buildings at Exhibition Place and Ontario Place is essential if they are to play a fuller role in the waterfront life of this region. The charming pavilions at the west end of Exhibition Place, complemented in modern form by the pods of Ontario Place, need ongoing activity if they are to remain viable in the long term. They could be considered as a site for an international institute, a group of writers, scholars or artists-in-residence, as the base for carrying out exchanges of students with Third World countries, as a haven for victims of torture or oppression, or for any number of other educational, humanitarian, and institutional uses.

Ultimately, these projects could be brought together to form a locally, nationally or even internationally important program devoted to educational, artistic, and humanitarian aims, perhaps supported by charitable and foundation donations.

Ontario Place, working within a more commercial framework, would benefit from greatly expanding its current functions to become a better-used conference and meeting centre.

~ Fifth, planning must take into account the need to increase business opportunities in the area. The major International Trade Centre proposed for the parking lots at the eastern open end of the Exhibition Grounds would generate new business opportunities; such state-of-the-art exhibition space is needed if the GTA, the Province of Ontario, and Canada are to remain competitive in world trade. Elsewhere, such centres generate substantial regional benefits: Chicago's McCormick Center, for example, produces close to $1 billion in direct income annually, and the Javits Center in New York generates $3.4 billion in direct and indirect income. Regional economic multipliers for European centres have been estimated at between four and six times. The proposed trade centre would generate additional benefits, including an increased number of visitors, and could be the catalyst that animates other parts of the area.

As de-industrialization of obsolete manufacturing plants occurs, the area could also become the locus for other private business investment opportunities, that, like the King Business Centre, would create jobs by building on and modernizing industrial heritage.

~ Sixth, it would be possible to permit appropriate infill development in keeping with the scale and character of the area, providing sites for new buildings that would help raise the level of activity and interest without compromising the essential park-like qualities of the area. New pavilion-in-the-park structures, hotels, and restaurants could be developed in conjunction with the trade centre and institutional uses described earlier.

Ontario Place's existing parking lots also present an opportunity for hotel or recreational development, adding to the site's critical mass. Previous generations have constructed wonderful buildings in parks, as both Ontario Place and Exhibition Place attest — surely, we can find lively and humane ways of expressing the values of our own times. To make room for such new uses, some of the less attractive buildings on the Exhibition Grounds could be torn down — notably the Food Products, Better Living, and perhaps the Queen Elizabeth buildings.

~ Seventh, Exhibition Place, Ontario Place, and these other sites should be integrated with the surrounding waterfront and inland neighbourhoods. The master plan should ensure that the redeveloped area is well integrated with surrounding neighbourhoods — Niagara, for example — while protecting them from any adverse consequences — traffic and noise — of increased activity.

~ The last consideration of a master plan depends on the as-yet unknown response to Toronto's bid for the 1996 Olympic Games. A new Olympic Stadium would be a major attraction and have a radical effect on the centre of the site. Appropriately designed, it could link together the proposed International Trade Centre's buildings and might even accommodate some of its functions.

But if a new stadium is not built, an alternative strategy would be to demolish the existing Exhibition Stadium and provide a new park extending across a covered Lake Shore Boulevard to fully knit Exhibition Place and Ontario Place together. It should be a place of gardens and water, bringing the lake to the centre of the grounds, and should be used as a central location for the festivals previously mentioned.

Recommendations

49. An integrated master plan — focused on the environment, land use, facilities, transportation, and capital investment requirements — should be developed for Exhibition Place, Ontario Place, Fort York, HMCS York, and neighbouring lands.

50. The plan should be developed on the basis of the considerations outlined on pages 124 to 128 above.

51. The plan should be available for consideration by the councils of Metropolitan Toronto, the City of Toronto, and the Province of Ontario, no later than 31 May 1991. The Royal Commission advises that it has included this matter in its fall 1990 work plan.

HARBOURFRONT

In Chapter 2 of its first interim report, released in August 1989, the Royal Commission made three recommendations on the future of this important area of the Central Toronto Waterfront:

1. Harbourfront Corporation should be converted immediately to a new entity, Harbourfront Foundation, whose mandate will be to continue the provision of Harbourfront's wide variety of outstanding cultural, recreational, and educational programs, generally by:
   a) programming its own activities;
   b) providing facilities and support to other organizations who wish to use its amenities and expertise;
   c) funding other organizations' programs which, in the opinion of the Board of Directors, are in the public interest and are compatible with a waterfront environment;
   d) placing a stronger emphasis on marine and water-related programs and activities;
   e) reflecting, maintaining, and preserving Toronto's waterfront and marine heritage;
   f) endowing the foundation sufficiently to sustain the continuation of Harbourfront's programming activities.

   The Commission also recommends that the Board of Directors and staff of Harbourfront Corporation be invited to become the Board and staff of the new foundation; and that the Board be expanded to include community representatives, representatives of user groups, and representatives of appropriate municipal governments.

2. The Harbourfront lands and properties should be planned with the City in accordance with the following principles:
   a) a minimum of 16 hectares (40 acres) of land made available immediately

for parkland and conveyed to the City, including a continuous waterfront promenade along the water's edge;

b) provision of a community school site (acceptable to the appropriate school board) to serve the Harbourfront community and the surrounding area, for conveyance to the school board;

c) provision of community facilities, including, but not necessarily limited to, a community centre, medical clinic, library facilities, day-care and play space for children, and a place of worship;

d) completion of Harbourfront Corporation's commitments with respect to assisted housing;

e) allocation of sufficient lands and properties to support the Harbourfront Foundation's programming mandate, as defined in Recommendation 1 above, and including additional program facilities, such as:

  i) a nautical centre, with sufficient space to provide permanent accommodation for the sailing clubs and schools currently operating out of makeshift facilities at Harbourfront; and

  ii) preservation of the Canada Malting silos, and consideration of their conversion to a civic museum;

f) further planning and development of Harbourfront land, including links to adjacent areas such as Coronation Park, Molson's, Dylex, Loblaws, SkyDome, the Railway Lands, the financial district, and the Central and East Bayfront, to be included in the City's review of the Central Area Plan;

g) no further building south of Queen's Quay West, with the exception of low-rise buildings considered by the City to be in the public interest;

h) an urban design plan to be established as an integral part of Harbourfront's Official Plan amendments. This plan should incorporate ideas such as those proposed by Gary Hack in a report to the Minister of Public Works, which deals with the need for visual coherence, and proposals put forward by Harbourfront's design panel on the need for a distinctive architecture appropriate to a setting along the water's edge and for special treatment of Queen's Quay West. The plan should also attempt to capture Eberhard Zeidler's principles, outlined in a submission to the Commission, which spoke of bringing back the "romance that is the key draw of the harbour, the age-old fascination of mankind with water".

3. The federal government should work with the City, the Harbourfront Foundation, and other appropriate bodies to give effect to the changes arising from these recommendations. The lands, properties, and residual interests now managed by Harbourfront Corporation, and those still in the inventory of Public Works Canada, should be held and administered by PWC on a temporary basis until appropriate agreements with the City are implemented.

In the year since then, significant progress has been made on all these recommendations.

First, the Government of Canada responded immediately to the Royal Commission through a statement issued by the President of the Treasury Board on 30 August 1989, which said the government was in substantial agreement with the Commission's proposals for Harbourfront.

It then moved quickly to examine ways to implement those recommendations by establishing a committee of officials and commissioning a valuation of the federal lands by independent consultants. In the spring of 1990, the government received a report from the Province on how to implement the changes, which it is now considering in tandem with its own ideas. Shortly thereafter the federal government appointed

Darcy McKeough to assist with implementation. Finally, on 31 May 1990, the government introduced legislation in the House of Commons (Bill C-73), to enable the federal Minister of Public Works to procure the dissolution of Harbourfront as a federal Crown corporation.

The Province of Ontario demonstrated both its willingness to protect the public interest in the waterfront and its desire to co-operate with the Government of Canada and the City by enacting a Minister's Zoning Order for the Harbourfront site on 13 December 1989, when a previous City-imposed freeze was about to expire. The minister responsible, the Honourable John Sweeney, also asked a provincial review team to examine the issues and report to him on 31 March 1990. On 23 March 1990, Mr. Sweeney presented this report to the Honourable Elmer MacKay and the Honourable John McDermid, respectively Minister of Public Works and Minister of State for Privatization and Regulatory Affairs.

The City of Toronto also played a co-operative role, patiently waiting for both federal and provincial activities to reach the stage where meaningful consultation could begin among the federal government, the City, the Province, and Metro, leading to a final resolution of outstanding issues and agreement on a clear-cut plan to make the necessary changes.

At a council meeting in June 1990, the City signalled its broad support for the overall directions being taken by the Government of Canada and proposed by the Province, while also indicating that it feels there are a number of issues, such as provision of community facilities, still to be settled.

The board of directors of Harbourfront Corporation, at their June meeting, voted unanimously to change the organizational basis of the corporation, and to concentrate the new organization's mandate solely on programming.

Implementation of the Royal Commission's recommendations is proceeding and, therefore, no further recommendation from the Commission is deemed necessary in this report.

Lake Shore Road, Toronto, early 1900s, Edwardian postcard

The Royal Commission commends all three governments — the Government of Canada for leadership, and the Province, City, and Harbourfront's board of directors for their co-operative support of the federal actions over the past year — and looks forward to the successful resolution of the Harbourfront situation.

THE RAILWAY LANDS

A Historical Overview

Discussion on the future of the Railway Lands is hardly a recent phenomenon: the idea of removing the 80 hectares (200 acres) of tracks separating the City from the lake has challenged planners, architects, developers, citizens, and politicians almost continuously for the past 30 years — and is hardly unique to Toronto. But a clear knowledge of the history of these lands is crucial to understanding where we are today, and what opportunities the future holds.

The first significant report on the lands in recent history was prepared in 1962 for the City of Toronto Planning Board; called *The Core of the Central Waterfront*, it suggested decking the rail corridor and creating an expanded terminal. This idea was embodied in the 1963 Plan for Downtown Toronto, ultimately adopted by City Council in 1965. At the time, both CN and CP were building major new freight yards in the suburbs and, in 1968, the railways jointly produced a study, *Metro Centre*, for the redevelopment of 80 hectares (200 acres) of land. Under it, the railway corridor to the south would be relocated, Union Station would be demolished, and a new intermodal transportation terminal, with significant commercial and residential development, would be built. Thus began the three-decade debate that persists to this day.

The Past

The arguments, however energetic, are only the most recent manifestations of a controversy that is much older: Toronto, after all, began on the lake and the waterfront has always been a pervasive and controversial factor in the City's development. Following the early years of colonial military rule, public and private interests were responsible for development on the waterfront.

Virtually all the Central Waterfront, starting at Front Street, was created by extensive landfilling that began in the early days of the City. In the 1830s, public concern about the use of, and access to, the waterfront made the city council of the day apply for the patent of the waterlots, south of the former shoreline, to create a public, 30-metre (100-foot) wide, tree-lined promenade. Construction of this esplanade — The Esplanade — did not begin for another 20 years, because of wrangles between the municipality and various private interests. However, less than two years after the opening of The Esplanade in 1854, the City granted the southern 12 metres (40 feet) of this strip to the Grand Trunk Railway (now CN).

In 1855, a new railway station was built at Front and Bay streets. Lakefilling for the railways, shipping, and industry continued, off and on, for the next 50 years. The many east-west railway tracks crossing the bottom of the busy city created dangerous and inconvenient level crossings at York, Bay, and Yonge streets. In 1892, a bridge was built over the tracks at York, permitting pedestrian and vehicular access to the waterfront and finally minimizing the effect of the rail barrier.

In 1904, the train station burned down in the Great Toronto Fire. Between 1905 and 1924, arguments continued among the CP and Grand Trunk railways, the City, the Toronto Harbour Commissioners, and the federal government — the subject: design and location of the station and a raised or lowered rail corridor. The Grand Trunk Railway supported the concept of raising the tracks on a viaduct — allowing York, Bay, and Yonge streets to run under the tracks — a plan CP opposed. Its response was to build its own station at Summerhill and Yonge, subsequently vacated.

Finally, in 1924, an independent commission recommended that the viaduct plan be implemented and the railway corridor was raised approximately six metres (20 feet). In 1927, Union Station as we know it today was opened, and more than 40 hectares (100 acres) of new land south of the station were created for rail yards. The freight line bypass along the southern boundary, also on a raised viaduct, was constructed and then filled in to create a berm six metres (20 feet) high.

In the 1930s, and for the next 30 years, the THC continued its massive program of lakefilling south of the Railway Lands, for port and industrial uses. Lake Shore Boulevard was constructed and, in 1963, the Gardiner Expressway opened. By then, the barriers to the waterfront, which we know so well today, were firmly in place: the railway corridor and rail yards were functioning on lakefill six metres (20 feet) above the water, and the Gardiner/Lake Shore Corridor was operational. It is ironic that, just as the railways were making plans to relocate their yards to the suburbs, Metropolitan Toronto, assuming the status quo, was building another waterfront barrier, the Gardiner Expressway.

Recent History: The 1970s
The two railways jointly created a development company (Metro Centre) and presented a plan to the City for 81 hectares (200 acres) of land owned by CN, CP, THC, the City, Metro, and the federal government. Not surprisingly, the issue of land ownership and control continually plagued plans.

The Metro Centre proposal was negotiated with the City, Metro, and the provincial government for four years and, by 1972, the Ontario Municipal Board had approved the plan for these lands. That year, construction started on the CN Tower, CP having backed out of the joint venture.

In 1973 and 1974, further public discussion and negotiations between government officials and the railways on implementing aspects of the project were conducted. A study carried out for the City concluded that Union Station could be retained as a transportation terminal, virtually eliminating the rationale for relocating the rail corridor to the south. The federal government's interest in the Railway Lands increased with the proclamation of Bill C27, the *Railway Relocation Act.*

This act provided federal financial assistance to local governments for relocating redundant or under-utilized rail lines and facilities which impeded the proper planning and development of Canada's urban centres.

In November 1974, CN announced that the Metro Centre project would be shelved, thus setting the stage for a new series of negotiations: the Premier of Ontario promptly convened a tri-level meeting, which set up the Toronto Transportation Terminal Task Force, primarily to deal with regional transportation issues (e.g., GO Transit). Two task forces were set up: an Implementation Committee to design and implement improvements to the rail corridor and Union Station; and a Land Use Committee to assess the implications of those improvements for development.

The federal government was effectively shut out of these discussions, although it did set aside $250,000 for a study to assess the barriers separating the Railway Lands and Harbourfront — a study that was never carried out. In the meantime — January 1976 — the City adopted a new Central Area Plan, which called for special studies of the Railway Lands.

The railways argued at the OMB that the plan was unacceptable and, by January 1978, Toronto City Council had proposed amendments to the Central Area Plan to deal with the railways' objections; it submitted two new studies, *The Railway Lands: Basis for Planning* and *The Railway Lands: Proposed Goals and Objectives*. These reports were adopted by City Council after four months of public discussion.

Recent History: The 1980s
With the Central Area Plan approved by the OMB in June 1978, the Railway Lands

Farm country in Newcastle

Steering Group was set up, chaired by the Honourable John Clement and comprising representatives of all the governments, as well as of the railways, to conduct detailed studies and co-ordinate the efforts of the many interested parties. By May 1982, the City Department of Planning and Development had submitted a progress report, which effectively launched the formal preparation of the new Railway Lands Part II Plan.

The fact that the City, rather than the railways, had initiated the plan was significant, as was the case it made for the Metro Centre. It is also important to note that the implementation of the plan (i.e., building infrastructure, land exchanges, cost-sharing) was an integral component of the approval of the plan. A series of background studies were prepared and circulated for public comment, leading to the *Railway Lands Part II: Development Concept* report in September 1983 and many public hearings that fall.

Work continued on preparation of the Part II Plan, which was submitted in March 1985; public meetings were held that spring. The final report for the Official Plan and Zoning By-law was submitted in July that year, followed in August by a report on the Memorandum of Conditions, which dealt with implementation aspects of the plan (land exchanges, infrastructure, cost-sharing, etc.).

The agreed Part II Plan set out Council's policy for the Railway Lands as follows:

... the Railway Lands are to be developed as an integral part of the central area so that the barrier effects of the road and rail corridor will be minimized and the central city reunited with the waterfront.

... the Railway Lands should satisfy a broad range of commercial, residential, institutional, cultural, recreational and open space needs, while ensuring effective and efficient transportation services, including inter-city rail and commuter rail services.

The plan divided up the 81 hectares (200 acres) of Railway Lands into 14 precincts, including Precinct A (Stadium Precinct), and allowed for large assignments of density, particularly at the eastern end where the extension of the financial district into this area was envisaged, with buildings comparable in height to those now existing in the financial district.

A significant aspect of the planning approval process is the creation of holding by-laws ("H" designations) that necessitate study of significant issues (e.g., environment and transportation) before Council will permit the development of subject lands. Council viewed the use of holding by-laws as "fundamental to the proper planning and incremental development of the Railway Lands".

In January 1985, then-Premier William Davis announced that a new covered baseball stadium would be located on the Railway Lands. By August of that year, Council had adopted the Part II Plan, Zoning By-laws, and Memorandum of Conditions, and in March 1986, it approved the by-laws and agreements for the stadium. All of these by-laws were debated at the Ontario Municipal Board in the summer of 1986 and were approved in December of that year.

In June 1987, a report prepared by architect and planner Stephen G. McLaughlin for the federal Bureau of Real Property Management (BRPM) was submitted to the President of the Treasury Board of Canada; it raised issues and set out new opportunities for all federal lands in the Toronto region, with particular emphasis on the waterfront, including the Railway Lands and Harbourfront.

In 1988, CN and Marathon Realty, the real estate subsidiary of CP, submitted separate applications to develop certain portions of the land and requesting that the "H" designation be removed entirely from the Railway Lands.

By early 1988, the applicants, unable to get the City to respond, appealed to the OMB for a hearing. The third of September 1990 has been set for that hearing. Last April, City Council asked its Commissioner of Planning and Development for a report on processing applications for the Railway Lands, and on 25 May 1990, he submitted a report on the desirability of reviewing the Official Plan Part II for the Railway Lands.

His report recommended that the plan be reviewed, in order to consider the implications of a long list of changes that have occurred since it was adopted. These include:

~ the residential land market in the central area;
~ residential built form and urban design implications;
~ residential amenity and quality of life issues;
~ the impact on transportation of residential development;
~ the need for a new Union Station Master Plan;
~ the proposed expansion of the Convention Centre;
~ the impact of SkyDome;
~ possible changes in the Bathurst/ Strachan/Lake Shore area;
~ the new federal/provincial plan for Harbourfront;
~ the review of City Plan '91;
~ changing public priorities (e.g., the Healthy Toronto 2000 plan adopted by Council);
~ the proposed provincial purchase of Union Station and the Toronto Terminal Railways (TTR) Corridor;
~ GTA studies and their impact on the central area;
~ provincial initiatives in transportation (e.g., an expanded LRT).

The report stressed that this review does not necessarily mean revisions to the Part II Plan and Zoning By-law. On 29 May 1990, City Council authorized the review and

asked that a report be prepared on the work program and process to be followed in conducting it.

History has shown that controversy has always dogged these lands. The interests of the players (governments, railways, citizens) have varied over the years, as in the blistering row that followed the railways' plans to tear down Union Station.

In 1978, *The Railway Lands: Proposed Goals and Objectives* plan set the stage for the next ten years. It is obvious that many things have changed since then:

~ Harbourfront, as we imagined it in 1978, does not exist today.

~ SkyDome did not exist in 1978.

~ There is now talk of taking down the Gardiner Expressway.

~ The impact of Union Station and the TTR Corridor as a new public utility has not been assessed.

~ Provincial initiatives through the GTA did not exist in 1978, and the implications

Garden plots on Leslie Street, Port Industrial Area

of new urban structure concepts have not been assessed.

~ The future of the entire waterfront is now undergoing scrutiny.

~ Environmental concerns have a new, and significant, importance.

At the same time, it is essential to recognize the infrastructure improvements that have been completed. While planning and political debates have gone on, very significant physical changes have been under way — paid for, in the main, by the railways, according to the terms of the Memorandum of Conditions. There are still worthwhile opportunities, taking into account recent changes and the fundamental goal of improving access to the waterfront for all. Doing so would preserve, and perhaps enhance, the underlying economic value of these lands.

52. The 1978 *Railway Lands: Proposed Goals and Objectives* and the 1985 Railway Lands Part II Plan should be reviewed to evaluate the degree to which they reflect today's concerns and should be revised to allow for the changes that have occurred in the intervening years and for the broader waterfront vision now emerging.

53. Notwithstanding the review, the Province should conclude its negotiations and proceed immediately to purchase Union Station and the adjacent rail corridor, and convert them for use as the central intermodal transportation facility for the Greater Toronto Area, recognizing their strategic function and location.

EAST BAYFRONT/PORT INDUSTRIAL AREA

Future of the Port of Toronto and the THC

In its 1989 interim report, having held hearings on the role and mandate of the Toronto Harbour Commissioners, the Royal Commission made the following recommendations on THC and on the Port of Toronto:

~ The THC's responsibility, jurisdiction, and mandate to operate the Port of Toronto should be limited to operating the Port of Toronto in and for the interests of the City of Toronto. Its mandate should be completely separate from planning or developing lands that do not serve a port function on the waterfront.

~ In addition, there must be greater local control of waterfront planning and a better system of accountability, which will involve further amendments to the *Toronto Harbour Commissioners Act, 1911*. The Royal Commission will make more specific recommendations about such amendments.

~ The actual amount of land now needed to operate the Port, and the amount likely to be needed in future, should be defined after detailed analysis. The Royal Commission will return to this subject, too, in the second phase of its work.

~ A complete environmental evaluation of all THC lands should be undertaken immediately and should include tests of air, water, and soil quality, to identify and measure contaminants.

~ In order to facilitate co-operation and co-ordination among those with responsibilities for the future of the Toronto waterfront, the Royal Commission recommends that THC lands and adjacent provincial lands in the Central Waterfront be pooled to permit the governments of Ontario and Canada to jointly sponsor environmental evaluation of them. The Royal Commission recommends that, while such an evaluation is being conducted, the Province use its powers under Section 3 of the *Planning Act, 1983* to declare a Provincial Interest, covering the combined lands as well as the headwaters and river valleys of the Toronto watershed.

On 30 August 1989, the day the interim report was released, the federal government declared that it supported the Commission's recommendations and indicated it was willing to pursue the transfer of lands no longer required for Port of Toronto purposes to another body.

Early last October, the provincial government responded positively as well by vesting this Commission with the powers of a Provincial Royal Commission; the Province then used its powers under the *Planning Act* to declare a Provincial Interest in the East Bayfront/Port Industrial Area and, with the federal government, jointly sponsored the recommended environmental audit of these lands. Phase I of the work concluded with

Intergovernmental environmental co-operation, Audit Progress Report Presentation, February 1990

publication of *Environment in Transition: A Report on Phase I of an Environmental Audit of Toronto's East Bayfront and Port Industrial Area*, Commission Publication No. 10.

Before considering port issues any further, it should be noted that the audit itself became an important vehicle for intergovernmental co-operation when both Metro and the City of Toronto decided to join it. That spirit was encapsulated in a meeting last February of federal and provincial ministers, Metro's chairman, and the Honourable David Crombie, at which the audit's steering committee presented its progress report.

Although the audit is not yet complete, it is evident from Phase I that cleaning up the area's contaminated soils presents a major challenge — one that must be met and overcome before re-use can proceed. In this respect, the East Bayfront/Port Industrial Area typifies a common problem faced by both public and private sectors throughout the Central Waterfront.

Even while the first phase of the audit was proceeding, the Commission was reviewing the overall role of ports in the Greater Toronto Area, particularly the transportation function of the Port of Toronto. The results were published as part of *Waterfront*

Transportation in the Context of Regional Transportation, Commission Publication No. 9. The analysis revealed that the Port of Toronto is smaller and less active than other Canadian ports — it ranks sixteenth nationally in tonnage — and actually serves a regional, rather than a national, role.

Studies show that the amount of needed marine terminal space varies by cargo level and type and that facilities for the following will be required in the Port of Toronto over the longer term:

general cargo	22 hectares	(55 acres)
cement	12 "	(30 ")
aggregates	10 "	(25 ")
salt	8 "	(20 ")
liquid bulk	8 "	(20 ")
sugar	6 "	(14 ")
grain	2.5 "	(6 ")
TOTAL	68.5 "	(170 ")

Not all of these facilities will or should be on land actually owned by the THC and there is no reason that the role private owners play in the functioning of the Port should change. Indeed, industries like Redpath Sugars should be encouraged to stay and it is likely that some other tenants or owners on the Ship Channel, or abutting the Turning

Basin, will want private marine terminal operations.

The possibility of establishing a consolidated cement/aggregate/ready-mix concrete complex near the east end of the Ship Channel has been studied in collaboration with the cement companies and is feasible. Consolidation would not be on THC lands, although, by contract, the THC could manage some or all marine terminal activity.

The port function will continue to be necessary as the Toronto waterfront accommodates industries and activities that need marine transportation and direct water access in order to serve the GTA market. The current checkerboard pattern of activity in the area means that land use is inefficient and precludes rational use of adjacent land, whether for port or alternate activities.

Clearly, port activities must be consolidated in the Port Industrial Area, which must be designed to accommodate current and future port uses, as well as other activity that may be identified as appropriate for the area. At the same time, the existing port terminals, which could handle more traffic, should be used more intensely, in order to increase their productivity; if traffic remains at current levels, it will require less terminal space.

Given the current mix of traffic moving through the Port, general cargo operations at MT 35, MT 51, and MT 52 could be consolidated at the MT 51 and MT 52 locations. Dry and liquid bulk cargoes already utilize the area adjacent to the Ship Channel and this use should continue, but could be consolidated for greater efficiency.

Recommendations

54. The Port of Toronto should be maintained and continue to operate as a regional port, retaining both public and private elements.

55. The federal government should enact amendments to the *Toronto Harbour Commissioners Act, 1911* necessary to consolidate all THC marine terminal activities on approximately 40 hectares (100 acres) of land, comprising MT 51/52 and adjoining lands on the south side of the Ship Channel (see Map 3). The balance of THC lands should be transferred as recommended herein.

56. The administration of the THC should be brought under the 1964 *Harbour Commissions Act*, to ensure that it is publicly accountable.

57. In view of the body of experience and staff expertise available at the THC, in addition to operating the marine terminals, the THC should be awarded contracts to perform a range of marine engineering, harbour mastering, navigation, and shipping activities along the Greater Toronto Waterfront.

The THC should maintain overall responsibility for harbour maintenance, including dockwall maintenance, harbour dredging, and harbour clean-up, as well as contractual responsibility for maintaining the infrastructure at the water's edge, for all other agencies along the waterfront. It should also continue to be responsible for ship safety and navigation within the harbour limits.

58. The mandate of the THC should be clearly defined, and supported by a strategically sound corporate/business plan that includes a corporate mission statement, objectives, and strategies for a five-year period. The corporate/business plan should also include a marketing strategy and staffing requirements.

59. Unless or until the levels of government responsible decide otherwise, the THC should continue to operate the Toronto Island Airport. (See recommendations, Chapter 1, *Interim Report*, 1989).

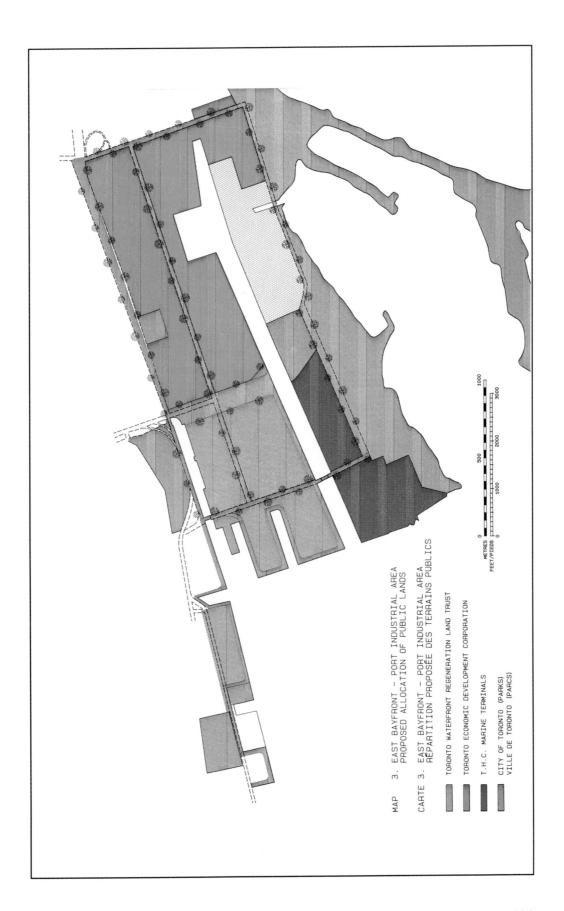

MAP 3. EAST BAYFRONT – PORT INDUSTRIAL AREA
PROPOSED ALLOCATION OF PUBLIC LANDS

CARTE 3. EAST BAYFRONT – PORT INDUSTRIAL AREA
RÉPARTITION PROPOSÉE DES TERRAINS PUBLICS

TORONTO WATERFRONT REGENERATION LAND TRUST

TORONTO ECONOMIC DEVELOPMENT CORPORATION

T.H.C. MARINE TERMINALS

CITY OF TORONTO (PARKS)
VILLE DE TORONTO (PARCS)

New Waterfront Parklands

The consolidation of the THC marine terminal activities and THC ownership in the southwest corner of the Port Industrial Area releases important land that can be used to pursue a number of remarkable new initiatives. Significant among these is the opportunity to create major new parklands along the central waterfront.

Recommendations

60. A continuous waterfront promenade (see Map 3) should be established along the entire East Bayfront and Port Industrial Area. The land would be conveyed to the City for parks purposes, making an important contribution to the Waterfront Trail recommended in this report, and would enable completion of this section of the Martin Goodman Trail.

61. Cherry Beach Park should be expanded (see Map 3) to comprise more than 80 hectares (200 acres). The land should be conveyed outright to the City and dedicated for parks purposes. The result: the Cherry Beach area would become one of the City's premier waterfront parks and, at the same time, the City would acquire a large new area east of the existing beach, land that connects to the Leslie Street Spit.

62. The Outer Harbour Marina Area should be conveyed to the City, to be developed as a waterfront park.

63. The Outer Harbour Marina should be conveyed to the City, limited to the existing 400 slips, and consideration should be given to having the THC manage the marina component on the City's behalf.

    These recommendations give the City ample opportunity to accommodate the needs, including security of tenure, of the member clubs of the Outer Harbour Sailing Federation.

64. A Don Valley Wildlife Corridor should be created, extending from the present mouth of the Don River to Unwin Street, forging a direct link from the Don Valley to the green space adjacent to the Leslie Street Spit (see Map 3). This land should be conveyed to the City as a park area, establishing the continuous wildlife corridor link that several deputants described as important to environmental regeneration of the area.

New Waterfront Industrial Park

The decision to consolidate THC ownership and activity not only creates the opportunity for significant new parklands, but also frees up and secures important lands for jobs, new enterprise, and economic development.

Recommendations

65. A new waterfront industrial park should be created in the East Bayfront/Port Industrial Area, in order to exploit the area's potential for thousands of waterfront jobs.

66. The Toronto Economic Development Corporation (TEDCO) is the appropriate agency to develop these lands for job creation; the Commission recommends that the area (see Map 3) bounded by the Don Valley Wildlife Corridor on the west and including all public lands north and east of the Ship Channel (except McCleary Park, which is to be retained by the City as a park) be conveyed to TEDCO.

In considering the economic future of Toronto, City Council, in February 1986, created the Toronto Economic Development

Corporation (TEDCO), which operates under a provincial charter; its mandate is to create jobs, particularly on under-utilized or surplus City property. Its board is made up of men and women from the business, labour, and public sectors. Its management is able to fast-track the development process because of its intimate knowledge of the City's administrative workings. While its mandate is city-wide, TEDCO clearly has particular importance in the future of the Central Waterfront.

TEDCO began as an offshoot of the Parking Authority of Toronto, itself an enormously successful business operation. (Now 30 years old, it has created assets worth almost $1 billion in current market terms, with virtually no outstanding debt. It pays business and realty taxes and a substantial annual dividend to the City of Toronto.) However, by the end of this year, TEDCO will have become independent of the Parking Authority, its senior management having had the advantage of the Authority's capability and expertise obtained during its association with the Authority.

TEDCO is now in the process of developing approximately 93,000 square metres (one million square feet) in three industrial projects and was also instrumental in establishing the recently opened Toronto New Business Development Centre.

TEDCO's mandate is currently under review and this may be the ideal time to consider the organization's role in revitalizing industry in the Central Waterfront, particularly in the East Bayfront/Port Industrial Area.

To be successful, industrial development agencies need to be at arm's length from the City and to have co-operation from municipal, business, and labour representatives. TEDCO is well placed in both these respects: while it is — and should continue to be — fully accountable to the City of Toronto, it does, indeed, enjoy an arm's-length relationship with the municipality. Clearly, its board should continue to include representatives from the City, Metro, business, and labour.

There are many opportunities on the waterfront for TEDCO: for example, it could collaborate with the World Trade Centre, which is part of a network of similar facilities in more than 50 countries. The importing and exporting of "green technology" could be considerably enhanced by the World Trade Centre's expertise in promoting international trade.

The Centre for Green Enterprise and Industry

Since the days when Toronto was founded on the shores of Lake Ontario, it has always sought and nurtured industry. That is no less true today than it was in 1805 when a certain Mr. Allen, Collector of Duties and Inspector

The method of land clearance that's currently practised in Richmond Hill has been termed the 'Atom Bomb' method of clearance because once it is complete, there is not a single identifiable feature left.

Marshall, S. 18 April 1990. "Presentation to the Royal Commission on the Future of the Toronto Waterfront public hearings on A Green Strategy for the Greater Toronto Waterfront." Transcript: public hearings on A Green Strategy for the Greater Toronto Waterfront, Toronto: Royal Commission on the Future of the Toronto Waterfront (Canada).

of Port and Pearl Ashes and Flour, offered to buy the ashes he needed for his business from the 500 or so inhabitants of the little village of York. What has changed, however, is the nature of industry — not just in Toronto, but throughout the western world. In the 150 years since the Industrial Revolution, industry has involved a natural resource, a hard worker, a machine, and a factory.

It still does. However, now we also have what is referred to as "new industry" — where jobs are based on, and contributing to, knowledge and information. These are industries without smokestacks, but with many opportunities for skilled blue- and white-collar workers; in fact, they include some of the fastest growing companies anywhere in the world. They are not water-dependent — but because they are environmentally friendly and/or environment-related, they are essential to the kind of waterfront envisioned in the work and recommendations of this Commission.

The key to the burgeoning environmental industries sector is the recognition that current environmental problems are an opportunity to profit — quite literally — from past mistakes. There is a need for new products and processes that will repair existing environmental damage and prevent it in the future — everything from industrial scrubbers to environmentally friendly diapers. That summons is already being taken up, with impressive results. According to estimates, there are now more than 3,000 companies in Canada, generating more than $7 billion annually, that say they offer environmental products and services. In the United States, environmental industries do $100 billion of business annually and are said now to constitute the country's third-largest industrial sector.

In Europe, an estimated two million jobs are associated with environmental industries. The changing face of Eastern Europe will probably raise that number rapidly. Furthermore, the industrialization of the Third World will create an enormous demand for environment-related products and services.

The July 1990 merger between France's second-largest construction company, Dumez, and its second-largest water utilities concern, Lyonnaise des Eaux, creating one of the world's largest "green" industrial companies, is a good example of what is happening. The new company, Lyonnaise des Eaux-Dumez, will be involved in everything from street cleaning to water supply, waste removal, air purification, and creating green spaces and living areas. Twenty-seven per cent of its $15-billion 1990 sales will be derived from environmental management, 45 per cent from construction and development, and 21 per cent from electrical equipment distribution.

In order to play a major role in Canada's industrial future, Toronto needs to build and attract such industries — that is one of the jobs facing TEDCO. But merely competing for industry is not enough: Toronto has to be imaginative and daring enough to actually help create those industries and products — and the jobs attached to them. To do this, a plan must be formulated to provide a home for environment-related industrial research and development; to offer a place where the growing number of people interested in the environment can get some of their training and education; where innovative techniques and products can be developed, tested, and manufactured; and where specialists in environmental marketing and distribution can be headquartered.

Some of the industrial elements that might make up or contribute to a green industrial complex are already located in the Port Industrial Area: telecommunications, film and television; generation of electricity; construction waste recycling; etc. The Commission intensively explored the development possibilities for these and other industries in the area with government, business, labour and academic experts during two seminars on green enterprise and industry it sponsored over the winter and spring of 1989/90.

Rouge River stream studies

Sixteen Mile Creek at Lions Valley Park

As a result of these deliberations, the Commission has concluded that what is missing is a catalyst to bring the different sectors and interests together and to convert the potential for green enterprise and industry into reality — to help make the Toronto of the 21st century what it has always been: a location for enterprise and industry, a liveable, workable City.

The catalyst could be in the form of an institute or a Centre for Green Enterprise and Industry, with its own building(s) situated in TEDCO's new industrial park. Its mission would be to work with government, business, industry, labour, research scientists, environmentalists, and academic experts to promote such enterprise and industry in Toronto and in Canada.

It would seek out firms interested in research and development related to environmentally sound or environment-specific enterprise and industry. The centre should be offered as a milieu for Canadian and world-ranked scientists, as well as for those involved in federal and provincial green-industry development programs, under which research and environmental agencies can develop projects appropriate to the present and future needs and opportunities of the provincial and Canadian economies.

Among the federal agencies that should be encouraged to participate in and with the centre are: the Department of Industry, Science, and Technology; the Department of Energy, Mines, and Resources; the National Research Council (NRC); the Natural Sciences and Engineering Research Council (NSERC); and Environment Canada. Provincial agencies should include the Ministry of Trade and Technology; ORTECH INTERNATIONAL (formerly the Ontario Research Foundation); and the Ministry of the Environment.

The centre would explore the possibility of attracting companies or organizations interested in gathering and disseminating information on environment-related statistics, experience, and trends. In helping to establish environmental information banks, TEDCO should work with the United Nations Environment Programs (UNEP), as well as with other international and national agencies responsible for gathering, reporting, and monitoring environmental information.

It would offer its facilities for training and education based on an ecosystem approach, to enterprise and industry, to students at community colleges, and to university undergraduate and graduate programs, for those who plan careers in business or industry. In carrying out this part of its mandate for the Centre, TEDCO should collaborate with community colleges in the Greater Toronto Area, including Ryerson, George Brown, and Humber, and with universities throughout southern Ontario, including Trent, Toronto, York, Windsor, Waterloo, and Guelph, all of which provide such education. In doing so, the centre would offer opportunities for direct contact among students, R & D experts, managers, and workers in the green enterprise and industry so essential to Toronto's future.

~~~~~~~

Recommendations

67. The Centre for Green Enterprise and Industry should be created.

68. The Centre should be managed by the Toronto Economic Development Corporation.

69. The Centre should be given a mandate to:
    a) carry out research and development (R&D) that explores the relationship between the environment, enterprise, and industry, and fosters business and manufacturing practices and processes that are "environmentally friendly", based on "cradle-to-grave" analysis of all inputs, components, and processes;
    b) act as a centre for gathering, analysing, and disseminating environmental information, statistics, and trends;
    c) provide education and training, using a curriculum based on an ecosystem approach, to students at community colleges, and undergraduate and graduate university students who plan to pursue careers in business or industry.

Toronto Waterfront Regeneration Land Trust

Recommendation

70. The Toronto Waterfront Regeneration Land Trust should be created. The balance of existing THC lands not otherwise conveyed by preceding recommendations, and certain adjacent wholly owned provincial lands (see Map 3), should be conveyed to this non-profit, provincially incorporated agency. The Trust's mandate would be to:
    a) complete the environmental audit of the provincially designated area;
    b) proceed to the remediation of all lands under its ownership and then plan to provide for a range of mixed uses, all in a park-like, low-rise setting;
    c) co-ordinate the regeneration of contaminated lands along the Greater Toronto Waterfront.

All lands would be retained in the public domain forever with appropriate uses and leases to ensure that the land-use plans as approved by the City of Toronto are protected. After the remediation of the lands, which will be recommended by the Royal Commission's environmental audit, the

Land Trust would proceed to carry out full public consultation before any concept plan is adopted. The regeneration and use of these lands would allow essentially vacant, unattractive, and under-utilized lands to be converted to productive lands that would create opportunities for thousands to live, work, and play along the Central Waterfront and adjacent lands.

The Toronto Waterfront Regeneration Land Trust would be subject to all normal City of Toronto planning controls and have appointees on its board of directors from the City, Metropolitan Toronto, and the Province, but it would clearly be legally accountable to the Province of Ontario. The mandate of the Toronto Waterfront Regeneration Land Trust should be clearly defined, supported by a strategically sound corporate/business plan clearly establishing a corporate mission statement, objectives, and strategies for a five-year period. The corporate/business plan should also include a marketing strategy and an outline of staff level requirements.

Vesting these lands in a provincial agency should facilitate the significant transportation and infrastructure changes that will be required for the area, as recommended in this report. It would also assist in their regeneration, as considerable initial cost will be incurred. One approach to the issue of soil decontamination could be for the Trust to enter into a joint venture with a company specializing in this business.

Cleaning Up the Don Valley
Environmental conditions in the East Bayfront/Port Industrial Area cannot be regenerated in isolation from the necessary clean-up of the Don River watershed. The City of Toronto's Don River Task Force is an important initiative, and deserves the gratitude of all those who care about the Don, about the City, and about the environment. But this group cannot be expected to carry out all the work that must be done.

Moreover, an ecosystem approach is essential: all municipal and other governments and agencies that have jurisdiction along the 38-kilometre (23-mile) length of the Don River will have to come together to develop a genuinely comprehensive remediation plan — and then implement it.

The jurisdictions in this valley include those of a number of federal and provincial agencies, two regional government bodies — Metro and York — and eight local municipalities — Toronto, York, East York, North York, Scarborough, Markham, Vaughan, and Richmond Hill — with a population of 930,000 people, a quarter of all those who live in the Greater Toronto Area.

The Toronto Waterfront Regeneration Land Trust could be the suitable body to help co-ordinate an ecosystem-wide approach to the Don clean-up. Until it is created, the Royal Commission will bring together all stakeholders and concerned agencies in the watershed to assist in developing a co-ordinated approach.

~

Recommendation

71. All levels of government and agencies with responsibilities for lands abutting the Don River should co-operate to develop a comprehensive clean-up plan for the Don River, and they should implement such a plan with an appropriate sense of urgency.

GREENWOOD RACETRACK
Greenwood Racetrack is located at the entrance to Toronto's Beach neighbourhood, occupying a 32.4-hectare (80-acre) block bordered by Queen Street, Woodbine Avenue, Lake Shore Boulevard, and Coxwell Avenue. The Ontario Jockey Club owns 26.3 hectares (65 acres) of the property; the balance is owned in two parcels by the City and Metro. These 6.1 hectares (15 acres) are currently used for parking.

There are a number of reasons to consider whether the site should be redeveloped in a way that helps meet public objectives in the Central Waterfront. *Housing and Neighbourhoods: The Liveable Waterfront*, Commission Publication No. 2, proposed that a new neighbourhood of approximately 3,000 residential units, many of which would be allocated for non-profit housing, might be created on this site, when it was no longer being used for racing. Moderate densities would make the development suitable for families, singles, and seniors and would be in keeping with the scale of the existing residential community.

In addition to being home to the 6,000 to 8,000 people who would live in the buildings, most of which would be low-rise, the site is large enough to accommodate a local park as well as such community facilities as a school and a senior citizens' community centre (identified by a local seniors' organization as needed). Public parking would be included at the south end of the site, to be used by those visiting nearby Ashbridge's Bay Park, Woodbine Pool, the Eastern Beaches, and the Queen Street restaurant and retail attractions.

Housing and Neighbourhoods: The Liveable Waterfront concluded that the beneficial effects of improving the congested parking situation in the local area, and improving open-space links to the waterfront for the residential areas to the north and west, would contribute positively to the surrounding neighbourhoods. Transportation would be provided by the Queen streetcar line at the north end of the site and the proposed LRT terminus.

Zoning in the proposed community would have to be identical with that in the Beach, and development would be structured by the southward extension of Lake Street and Lockwood, Brookmount, and Rainsford roads. These north-south streets would terminate at a westward extension of Kew Beach Avenue, in order to extend the quality and nature of the adjacent residential neighbourhoods to the new development.

It has been suggested that a direct south-westerly extension of Kingston Road, linking with Lake Shore Boulevard at Coxwell Avenue, would further reinforce this objective and would make Woodbine Avenue south of Queen Street and the existing Lake Shore Boulevard east of Coxwell less formidable and more in keeping with the tone of adjacent neighbourhoods.

There are few opportunities left in the GTA for large, residential developments on the waterfront. The Task Force on the Gardiner/Lake Shore Corridor has recommended that the 6.1-hectare (15-acre) parking site be redeveloped for housing and a public parking structure. If the Ontario Jockey Club and the Province should agree on an alternate, more suitable location for the racetrack, there would be an opportunity for redevelopment that could best be explored jointly by the City of Toronto and the Government of Ontario.

Recommendation

72. The Government of Ontario and the Ontario Jockey Club should continue discussions about the future of Greenwood Racetrack and, if the OJC moves elsewhere, the Province and the City of Toronto should enter into a partnership to develop the site.

5. City of Scarborough

Most of Scarborough's 20 kilometres (12 miles) of shoreline is given over to mature, residential neighbourhoods, and under-utilized industrial parks, including the Johns-Manville property in the Centennial area. Its waterfront includes the magnificent Scarborough Bluffs, the Rouge River area, and a series of parks.

The bluffs — striking visual evidence of the ice age that shaped Canadian geography

— restrict access to Scarborough's waterfront. Stretched across some 15 kilometres (nine miles) of shoreline, they rise as high as 100 metres (330 feet) above Lake Ontario. There are built obstacles as well: one of Metro's sewage treatment plants, the Guild Inn, and the CN rail line. Furthermore, private residential properties that extend to the bluffs' edge, and the fact that east-west roads are distant from the waterfront, also challenge those seeking public access to the top of the bluffs and to connections between existing parks and open spaces.

Guild Inn, East Point Park, and the Lower Rouge River.

The Province recently announced that it would create Rouge Park, which will be the largest urban park in Canada — a positive response to the Royal Commission's related recommendations in its 1989 interim report. The initiative, designed to protect and enhance the Rouge River Valley area, is both timely and necessary: the valleylands and Rouge River mouth need protection if their environmental stability, open space, and parkland are to be retained.

Controlling water levels with draining, Centennial Wetland in Scarborough

The public bodies most active on the Scarborough waterfront are the City and MTRCA, with Metro Toronto providing regional co-ordination. While the City of Scarborough is situated in three major watersheds — the Don and Rouge rivers and Highland Creek — most City shoreline and river valleys are either owned or managed by MTRCA or by Metropolitan Toronto's Parks and Property Department. The City of Scarborough owns only a few parks.

Existing parks and public recreational areas along the Scarborough waterfront include Rosetta McClain Gardens, Scarborough Heights Park, Bluffer's Park, the

Later this year, MTRCA is scheduled to have a revised draft Master Plan/Environmental Assessment document for East Point Park, which will be reviewed by various agencies and the public. It will be presented to MTRCA's Water and Related Land Management Advisory Board in November. The entire park proposal, which includes lake-filliing to create boat-launch facilities and a 600-slip marina, is subject to the *Environmental Assessment Act*.

Current proposals for access to Scarborough's waterfront include pedestrian access through the Brimley Road ravine to Bluffer's Park, and a trail system linking Highland Creek Marsh, East Point Park, and the Guild Inn. The Royal Commission supports these proposals, which

are compatible with its Waterfront Trail concept.

Green spaces along Scarborough's waterfront, including popular areas such as Bluffer's Park and Rosetta McClain Gardens, are currently just nodes, not linked to each other or to any other waterfront trail. Because of funding or other priorities of the City and of MTRCA, some of the open spaces and trail proposals have not materialized.

In 1989, Scarborough formed a Waterfront Committee, made up of seven City councillors, who hold regular meetings to address various shoreline issues; more recently, the group held public meetings to discuss the future of the City's waterfront. Local residents have expressed two main goals: to protect the waterfront as an environmental resource and to have lands retained or made available for appropriate passive recreational uses.

Public participation is important in determining the future of the waterfront not only because such participation is always of benefit, but, particularly in this case, because so much waterfront land is currently in private hands; public input ensures that comprehensive waterfront policies — which are not part of Scarborough's Official Plan — are needed to ensure that appropriate waterfront goals are developed and attained.

A review/update of the 1959 Official Plan is being considered by the City and establishing appropriate waterfront policies could be part of such a review. The plan should also be linked to the Metropolitan Toronto Plan review and the proposed Metro Toronto Waterfront Plan.

~~~~~~

Recommendations

73. The Province of Ontario, the Regional Municipality of Metropolitan Toronto, and the City of Scarborough should negotiate a Waterfront Partnership Agreement in conjunction with appropriate authorities and agencies. The agreement,

A public port is charged with operating in the public interest. It must be attentive to new ideas and opportunities, and to changes in the community's values.

Hershman, M. J. and R. Scott Bittner. 1988. "Ports over time: historical perspectives on the public port." In *Urban ports and harbor management: responding to change along U.S. waterfronts*, editor M. J. Hershman. 52. New York: Taylor & Francis.

which should be the foundation of a future waterfront plan, should include the following:

a) It should clearly identify the roles and responsibilities of various agencies and authorities in developing and implementing plans for the Scarborough waterfront; the lead role in local waterfront planning should remain in the hands of the City of Scarborough, with Metro playing a regional co-ordinating role. MTRCA should be encouraged to continue its role.

b) It should contain comprehensive waterfront and river valley policies, conforming to the principles of this report and taking into careful account the environmental vulnerability of the Scarborough Bluffs and the Rouge River Valley area; such policies should also outline ways to acquire, maintain, and provide access to land along the waterfront and up the river valleys; these policies could take the form of a waterfront plan and should be incorporated into the City's official and secondary plans.

Until that is done, interim waterfront policies should be prepared and adopted by the City with input from the Scarborough Waterfront Committee and from appropriate authorities and agencies. Such policies should be guided by the development principles produced earlier this year by the City's planning department and should conform to the principles in this report.

c) It should make provision for additional funding for MTRCA, to enable it to continue land acquisition and development of projects on the Scarborough section of Metro Toronto's waterfront, to be maintained by Metro's Parks and Property Department.

d) It should continue to develop a Waterfront Trail system, recommended earlier in this report, placing priority on enhancing access nodes to the waterfront and on improving access to Bluffer's Park. Where possible, the Trail should also include a component for educating the public on the geological processes that contributed to formation of the bluffs.

e) It should explore the possibility of extending the Martin Goodman Trail from the eastern boundary of Toronto to Scarborough; such a plan should be incorporated into the proposals for a Waterfront Trail system.

f) It should negotiate with CN/CP for vehicular and pedestrian access south of the rail lines in the Port Union area; where possible, such access should be included as a condition for private development or redevelopment along the waterfront.

g) It should include redevelopment of such previously industrial areas as the Johns-Manville site; they offer the opportunity to establish a new residential area, the Port Union community, on the Scarborough waterfront. The City of Scarborough should investigate the potential of doing so with CN/CP, private property owners, and MTRCA, and results should be included in future planning documents. An environmental assessment should be undertaken, under the *Environmental Assessment Act,* of the Johns-Manville and other industrial sites before they are considered for redevelopment.

74. The City should be certain that local interests are fully considered when it is evaluating redevelopment proposals for the publicly owned Guild Inn site. In future, applications for development or redevelopment of land on the Scarborough waterfront should be evaluated by the City on the basis of waterfront policies or interim policies, and should conform to the principles of this report.

75. The draft East Point Park Master Plan/ Environmental Assessment should address issues of lakefill, road access, traffic and safety, and the project's environmental impact, during the construction phase and following park completion, to the satisfaction of all agencies involved and interested members of the public. The plan should conform to the principles espoused by the Royal Commission.

76. All lakefill proposals for the Scarborough waterfront — in respect of either development or erosion protection — should be subject to the comments on lakefill in this report.

6. Durham Region

The Region of Durham has many of the best remaining opportunities for protecting stretches of natural waterfront in the Greater Toronto Area. At the same time, however, that waterfront is controlled by a diverse array of institutions: one regional and five local municipalities, and three conservation authorities.

In the westerly part of Durham, the towns of Pickering and Ajax have traditionally relied on the Metropolitan Toronto and Region Conservation Authority to carry out waterfront planning, land acquisition, and development. Neither Pickering nor Ajax has prepared waterfront plans beyond those routinely prepared by the conservation authorities for its holdings.

However, the conservation authorities — particularly Central Lake Ontario and Ganaraska Region — have been constrained by lack of funding and local support. The GRCA's attention has been directed primarily to the headwaters. CLOCA developed a long-range waterfront plan in 1973, but its activity since then has focused primarily on Lynde Shores, the Oshawa Creek Valley, and Bowmanville Harbour.

In the Town of Whitby and the City of Oshawa, leadership on waterfront issues has effectively been assumed by the local municipal governments. Although Whitby has no comprehensive waterfront plan, it has dealt with its waterfront through its Official Plan and with the Lynde Shores Secondary Plan. In addition, the development of a major waterfront activity centre has been detailed in the Port Whitby Secondary Plan and the related draft Harbour Master Plan.

Oshawa recently approved a comprehensive waterfront development plan which calls for a system of linked waterfront parks. A major section of the City's waterfront, the Port of Oshawa, is currently under the control of the Oshawa Harbour Commission, a federal agency.

The Port is a relatively small commercial operation in an urban setting, adjacent to the Second Marsh, an environmentally sensitive area. It serves a local market and is attempting to expand its limited cargo base.

In October 1989, the City, concerned about planning in the Port and surrounding areas, imposed an Interim Control By-law, which has restricted development in the area. A comprehensive planning study for southeast Oshawa is to be undertaken on these lands, primarily to confirm the future role and function of the Oshawa Harbour; it will also resolve a number of land-use issues and identify the most appropriate development for the area.

At this time, there does not appear to be an agreed-on set of development objectives for the southeast Oshawa waterfront. Instead, the Oshawa community appears to be divided on the role of the Port area, between those who favour the traditional port function and those who foresee a waterfront that emphasizes open space, recreation, and alternate land uses including residential and light commercial development. Some believe the waterfront, including the Port, is an underdeveloped resource that must be revitalized.

There are also questions of the future uses or expansion of the St. Mary's Cement terminal in Bowmanville, but these cannot be resolved without further detailed analysis.

The Town of Newcastle has no comprehensive plan covering its entire waterfront, although official plan policies for the urban areas of the Town of Bowmanville and the Village of Newcastle deal with limited waterfront issues. In response to recreation and tourism proposals for the waterfront east of Bowmanville Harbour, the Town has initiated a waterfront study of that particular area.

However, a plan for the entire Newcastle waterfront is also needed, to address development opportunities in the best interests of the Town. This plan should not be simply reactive to private-sector proposals; rather, it should address the public interest in communities about to face the pressures of rapid urbanization. In that regard, it is vital that

Sundown at Ashbridge's Bay

the plan retain as much as possible of the currently undeveloped shoreline for future public use.

While plans to protect the public interest along the Durham waterfront are fragmentary, the forces threatening to diminish waterfront opportunities are mounting. It is expected that the population of Durham will increase by 65 per cent from 1986 to 2001, the greatest growth rate for any of the four regions on the Greater Toronto Waterfront.

Substantial portions of the waterfront are already blocked off by industrial or utility designation and use, as well as by considerable residential development. Proposals for new development along the waterfront are being submitted at an unprecedented rate.

Without decisive action, many opportunities for a green and accessible waterfront in Durham Region will be lost; clearly, an agency is needed to deal with the issue with a sense of urgency and the determination to protect the potential of the Durham waterfront.

Although the Commission recognizes and commends the excellent waterfront planning already under way in individual parts of Durham (Oshawa and Whitby), it believes that the issue has to be treated on a regional basis. The conservation authorities are not in a position to do so, in part because their jurisdictions fragment the region. Moreover, it was clear from the Commission's public hearings that CLOCA currently lacks the respect and public support necessary to be a leader in this matter.

In the Commission's view, leadership for the Durham waterfront should be assumed by the Region of Durham itself, which has limited waterfront policies, and is currently reviewing its Official Plan. In her remarks before the Commission, the chairwoman of the Regional Planning Committee said of the Region's role on the waterfront, "I think that the time is right for some new thinking and new direction."

That new thinking should help the Region of Durham develop a strong regional role as co-ordinator of waterfront activities, and become a proponent of protective waterfront policies. This does not mean

Increasingly, physical changes in the configuration and use of harbors and adjacent land areas have been subject to environmental constraints. Impacts of such changes upon ecosystems, both landward and in the waters, are major considerations in determining the feasibility and desirability of harbor and channel projects.

Mayer, H. M. 1988. "The physical harbour: new demands on a scarce resource." In *Urban ports and harbor management: responding to change along U.S. waterfronts*, editor M. J. Hershman. 90. New York: Taylor & Francis.

that the plans of local municipalities should be ignored — rather, they should be co-ordinated within a regional context and helped to become reality.

Recently, the Region began discussions with the Province and with local municipalities regarding development of a regional waterfront plan. While the Region's priority has been review of its Official Plan, it is important to recognize the significance of the waterfront in this context and the need for comprehensive policies as part of this plan and related documents.

Several issues could be particularly emphasized in a Durham waterfront plan. In several areas, protection of high-quality marshes and other natural areas demands attention, to prevent their loss to marinas, quarrying or other development. In order to protect some marshlands, controls are also needed on adjacent land development that might cause the loss of habitat quality as the result of stormwater inflows, lack of buffers or excessive traffic.

There are also the issues of creating appropriate links past several major industrial and utility sites, and of finding the right scale and balance of residential and recreational developments and their timing.

Recommendations

77. As recommended by the Region of Durham, the Province should declare the Durham waterfront an area of Provincial Interest under the *Planning Act*.

78. The Province should negotiate a Waterfront Partnership Agreement with the Region of Durham, other levels of government and their agencies, and appropriate private-sector interests, to govern future activity along the waterfront. (Because various municipalities in the Region are at different stages of waterfront planning, several area-specific agreements may be required for the short

term.) The Waterfront Partnership Agreements should be closely linked to preparation of a Durham Waterfront Plan, and should include:

a) provision for financial assistance to the Region and local municipalities to prepare or extend comprehensive waterfront plans;

b) mechanisms to obtain commitments of substantial, multi-year provincial funding to support public acquisition and development of waterfront natural areas, recreation sites, and links;

c) provisions that ensure the Durham Waterfront Plan and local plans conform to the ecosystem approach and principles outlined in this report;

d) clear identification of the roles and responsibilities of various agencies in implementing waterfront plans in Durham, with Durham Region taking the co-ordinating role;

e) clarification of the roles of conservation authorities, giving them expanded powers to regulate shoreline and valleyland development based on ecological and recreational objectives, as well as account for flood and erosion protection;

f) a review of proposed regional water and sewer facility plans along the waterfront, to ensure that their location and design do not detract from other waterfront objectives;

g) strategies to maintain and protect significant natural habitats, including:
   ~ Frenchman's Bay marshes;
   ~ Carruther's Creek mouth;
   ~ Lynde Creek mouth;
   ~ Pumphouse Marsh;
   ~ Oshawa Second Marsh;
   ~ McLaughlin Bay;
   ~ West Side Beach Marsh;
   ~ Wilmot Creek mouth; and
   ~ Bond Head Bluffs;

h) identification of opportunities and plans to maintain or create green corridors up the valleys of Duffin Creek, Lynde Creek, Oshawa Creek, Bowmanville/Soper Creek, Wilmot Creek, and the Ganaraska Valley, and to protect the natural values of other valleylands such as Petticoat Creek, Carruther's Creek, and Graham Creek;

i) a land-use concept study of Frenchman's Bay and the surrounding lands to determine how the ecosystem approach and principles would apply to potential land uses there;

j) plans to establish substantial community forests in the urban separators defined by the Region of Durham, and a major new park on the west side of Lynde Creek, as proposed by the Town of Whitby;

k) details of a Waterfront Trail route, noting in particular the challenges provided by Ontario Hydro, the Pickering and Darlington generating stations, and St. Mary's Cement;

l) plans for protecting the West Side Beach Marsh and creating a suitable buffer area in relation to continued quarry operations;

m) plans to modify the pattern of development and stormwater outlets proposed in the Lynde Shores Secondary Plan, to satisfy the Ministry of Natural Resources, the conservation authorities, and the Durham Region Field Naturalists that no long-term damage will occur to the Lynde Shores Marsh;

n) incorporation of the concept of continuous public access to the waterfront in Whitby Harbour, in line with the principles outlined earlier in this report;

o) the transfer of the Class 3 wetland at the mouth of Carruther's Creek and a suitable buffer, to be managed by a public agency as a protected wetland, and acquisition of waterfront lands east of the creek by the Town of Ajax or MTRCA, as a requirement of future development;

p) updating of the 1984 *Oshawa Harbour Development Plan*, which was created by Transport Canada, the Oshawa Harbour Commission, and the City of Oshawa, in order to define the Port's role on the waterfront; the traditional port function should be examined in light of the potential for alternate land uses and development, and plans for the future of the Southeast Oshawa waterfront must be developed and implemented; if it is determined that the industrial commercial port function is no longer warranted, the Oshawa Harbour Commission should be disbanded and its lands transferred to the City of Oshawa for development based on an approved plan and conforming to the principles espoused in this report;

q) suspension of any approvals for proposed residential, commercial, industrial, tourism or recreational projects along the Newcastle waterfront until a plan for its entire length has been approved or until it can be ascertained that such proposals are in conformity with the principles of the plan and those contained in this report.

THE PICKERING LANDS

Several deputants directed the Commission's attention to the block of federal and provincial lands originally assembled for the proposed Pickering airport and adjacent urban development. These lands, which total approximately 16,187 hectares (40,000 acres), are located just east of the Rouge Valley. (Superimposed on a map of Toronto, they would cover an area from the Toronto Islands to Steeles Avenue, and from High Park to Greenwood Avenue.) They are entirely publicly owned, and are now managed under short-term leases.

The federal government is considering disposing of half of its 7,527 hectares (18,600 acres), retaining the other half for a possible future airport. The Province recently unveiled plans to develop some 2,833 hectares (7,000 acres) of their holdings as the Seaton townsite. Most of the federal and provincial lands at the Pickering site are eminently suitable for agriculture, and include a mosaic of high-quality natural areas and valleylands.

As Lorne Almack of the Pickering Rural Association pointed out:

> This is no ordinary piece of real estate; it is green. We the people of Ontario and Canada, own it. We are free to make intelligent decisions as to its use, and we can demonstrate our concern for the environment.

The Commission agrees that the legacy of federal and provincial lands at Pickering offers a unique opportunity for both levels of government to lead by example. Present management by short-term lease, which leads to abuse of agricultural lands and environmental deterioration, must be improved. Selling off lands to the highest bidder, which would continue the pattern of adjacent suburban sprawl, would squander an opportunity to provide a better model for future use of near-urban open space.

The root of many concerns about the future of these lands is the lack of clarity and co-ordination between the provincial and federal governments regarding their long-term intentions. After nearly two decades of public ownership, it would seem reasonable to expect that both governments could decide what their future needs are for the properties involved, and could work together to plan management or disposal of surplus lands.

By announcing its plans for the "environmental city" of Seaton on part of the Pickering site, the Province has already accepted the principle of innovative use of the lands in the public interest. The Commission applauds the Province's decision to

Towards Lake Ontario, at Newcastle

embark on this important initiative. Planning for Seaton must ensure that the commendable concept of the environmental city does not deteriorate and lead to simply another sprawling bedroom community. It is essential that the densities and patterns of development allowed in Seaton support necessary services, and demonstrate the environmental advantages of a compact urban form. But planning should go one step further, to place the environmental city in an environmentally sustainable countryside.

Recommendations

79. The federal and provincial governments should co-operate in planning co-ordinated future uses of the Pickering lands, and in managing or disposing of lands surplus to their needs.

80. The federal and provincial governments should co-operate to ensure that portions of the lands are used for agricultural purposes and create a living, functioning countryside, in which there is special emphasis on practices that sustain the environment and preserve future options for a green gateway to the city.

WATERSHED

The Greater Toronto Region is, both literally and figuratively, at a watershed. Not long ago, society believed that the environment was endlessly able to absorb the detritus of a modern, industrial-based economy. More recently, the assumption was that the environment and the economy were inevitably opposed: opting for one meant damaging the other.

Today, however, it is clear that the two, rather than being mutually exclusive, are mutually dependent: a good quality of life and economic development cannot be sustained in an ecologically deteriorating environment.

The way we choose to treat the Greater Toronto Waterfront is crucial. If governments and individuals recognize — and act on — the need to resolve past environmental problems and forge strategies to protect the waterfront now and in the future, we will, indeed, have successfully crossed a watershed.

— David Crombie

APPENDICES

APPENDIX A

ORDERS-IN-COUNCIL

P.C. 1988-589

Certified to be a true copy of a Minute of a Meeting of the Committee of the

Privy Council, approved by Her Excellency the Governor General

on the 30th day of March, 1988.

WHEREAS there exists a historic opportunity to create a unique, world class waterfront in Toronto;

AND WHEREAS there is a clear, public understanding that the challenge can only be achieved with more cooperation among the various levels of government, boards, commissions and special purpose bodies and the private sector;

AND WHEREAS the Intergovernmental Waterfront Committee has identified a number of urgent matters that must be studied and dealt with;

AND WHEREAS the Government of Canada has certain jurisdictional and property responsibilities in the area:

Now therefore, the Committee of the Privy Council, on the recommendation of the Prime Minister, advise that the Honourable David Crombie be authorized to act as a Commissioner effective from June 1, 1988, and that a Commission, to be effective from that date, do issue under Part I of the Inquiries Act and under the Great Seal of Canada, appointing the Honourable David Crombie to be a Commissioner to inquire into and to make recommendations regarding the future of the Toronto Waterfront and to seek the concurrence of affected authorities in such recommendations, in order to ensure that, in the public interest, Federal lands and jurisdiction serve to enhance the physical, environmental, legislative and administrative context governing the use, enjoyment and development of the Toronto Waterfront and related lands, and more particularly to examine

(a) the role and mandate of the Toronto Harbour Commission;

(b) the future of the Toronto Island Airport and related transportation services;

(c) the issues affecting the protection and renewal of the natural environment insofar as they relate to federal responsibilities and jurisdiction;

.../2

P.C. 1988-589

- 2 -

(d)   the issues regarding the effective management of federal lands within the Toronto Waterfront area; and

(e)   the possible use of federal lands, facilities, and jurisdiction to support emerging issues, such as the proposed Olympic Games and World's Fair; and,

The Committee do further advise that the Commissioner

(a)   be directed to seek full consultation with all interested parties and especially the Province of Ontario and the City and Metropolitan Governments;

(b)   be authorized to adopt such procedures and methods as he may from time to time deem expedient for the proper conduct of the inquiry;

(c)   be assisted in the conduct of the inquiry, where appropriate, by the officers and employees of the various departments or agencies of the Government of Canada;

(d)   be authorized to sit at such times and in such places as may be required and to rent such space and facilities as may be required for his staff, in accordance with Treasury Board policies, in both Ottawa and Toronto;

(e)   be authorized to engage the services of such staff and technical advisors, including counsel, as he may consider necessary or advisable, at such rates of remuneration and reimbursement as may be approved by Treasury Board;

(f)   be authorized to engage the services of such experts and other persons as are referred to in section 11 of the Inquiries Act who shall receive such remuneration and reimbursement as may be approved by Treasury Board;

(g)   be authorized to publish special studies as may be appropriate from time to time and to submit interim reports to the Governor in Council as may be required;

...3

P.C. 1988-589

- 3 -

(h) be directed to submit his report in both
     official languages to the Governor in Council
     with all reasonable dispatch, but not later
     than June 1, 1991; and

(i) be directed to file the records and papers of
     the inquiry as soon as reasonably may be after
     the conclusion of the inquiry, with the Clerk
     of the Privy Council.

CERTIFIED TO BE A TRUE COPY - COPIE CERTIFIÉE CONFORME

CLERK OF THE PRIVY COUNCIL - LE GREFFIER DU CONSEIL PRIVÉ

Ontario
Executive Council

Order in Council

On the recommendation of the undersigned, the Lieutenant Governor, by and with the advice and concurrence of the Executive Council, orders that

WHEREAS the Province of Ontario recognizes the importance of the Interim Report and recommendations of the federal Royal Commission on the Future of the Toronto Waterfront, of which the Honourable David Crombie is Commissioner;

AND WHEREAS, in the spirit of returning the waterfront to the people, the Commissioner has recommended that there be intergovernmental management and co-operation, that the mandate of the Toronto Harbour Commission be refocussed and that the Toronto Harbour Commission lands and Provincial lands in the central waterfront be "pooled" for the purpose of carrying out a comprehensive environmental evaluation to assist in determining the most appropriate future uses of these lands;

AND WHEREAS the Commission's Interim Report acknowledges the environmental significance of the waterfront and the ecological dependence of the waterfront on the headwaters, source areas and river valleys which drain into Lake Ontario;

AND WHEREAS the Commission's Interim Report also recognizes the extensive socio-economic pressures which characterize waterfront development and the importance of rational planning and development of the waterfront on the future quality of life and well being of hinterland areas;

AND WHEREAS the Province of Ontario recognizes the Provincial interest in a number of key aspects of the Commission's next phase (Phase 2), including ensuring that the natural environment is fully considered and given due weight in any deliberations regarding future development options for the waterfront, that open space and continuous public access are fundamental components of future waterfront development and that transportation and broader quality of life issues associated with the sustainable socio-economic development of the fastest growing economic area of the country are effectively managed;

O.C. 2465/89

AND WHEREAS there are significant provincial land holdings which are integral to future waterfront development;

AND WHEREAS the Province of Ontario wishes to collaborate with the Federal Government in Phase 2 of the Royal Commission's work in order to achieve the objectives set out in the Royal Commission's Interim Report and to avoid any confusion regarding the position of the Province of Ontario on the need for coordinated and sensitive development of the waterfront and to avoid duplication in public hearings processes;

AND WHEREAS it is considered expedient to cause inquiry to be made under the Public Inquiries Act, R.S.O. 1980, c. 411 concerning the following matters associated with the Toronto Waterfront, which matters are hereby declared to be of public concern;

AND WHEREAS such inquiry is not regulated by any special law;

NOW THEREFORE pursuant to the provisions of the said Public Inquiries Act a commission be issued to appoint the Honourable David Crombie a Commissioner:

1. to inquire into and recommend initiatives to preserve and create continuous public access to the water's edge extending from the eastern boundary of the Region of Durham to the western boundary of the Region of Halton;

2. to inquire into and make an environmental evaluation of those Toronto Harbour Commission lands and adjacent Provincial lands recommended to be pooled in the aforesaid Interim Report;

3. to inquire into and make recommendations on issues associated with management and development of the pooled and other appropriate waterfront lands, including:

    (a) appropriate allocation of waterfront lands to various uses, i.e. housing, open space, industrial and commercial uses;

    (b)   waterfront transportation in the context of the regional transportation system;

    (c)   housing and community development on the waterfront; and

    (d)   employment and job opportunities relating to the waterfront;

4.   to inquire into and recommend waterfront related initiatives to preserve and enhance the quality of the environment and the quality of life for people residing in the greater metropolitan area extending from the eastern boundary of the Region of Durham to the western boundary of the Region of Halton;

5.   to inquire into and recommend financing proposals and other mechanisms to link and integrate the waterfront to the upstream watersheds in the aforementioned locations.

AND THAT the Commissioner shall complete his inquiry and assessment and make recommendations and deliver his report by June 1, 1991;

AND THAT all Government Ministries, Boards, Agencies and Commissions shall assist the Commissioner to the fullest extent in order that he may carry out his duties and functions, and that he shall have authority to engage such counsel, experts, technical advisors, investigators and other staff as he deems proper, at rates of remuneration and reimbursement to be approved by the Management Board of Cabinet;

Recommended _____ Concurred _____
         Minister of Municipal   Chairman
         Affairs

Approved and
Ordered _____ October 12, 1989 _____
           Date   Lieutenant Governor

APPENDIX B

REFERENCES

Baird/Sampson Urban Design Inc. and The Kirkland Partnership. 6 February 1990. *The Lower Yonge Street urban design study*, Toronto: Task Force on the Gardiner/Lake Shore Corridor.

Boardman, P. L. 1978. *The worlds of Patrick Geddes: biologist, town planner, re-educator, peace-warrior*, 3. London: Routledge and Kegan Paul.

Burns, R. 1969. "To a mouse, on turning her up in her nest, with a plough, November 1785." In *Burns' poems and songs*, J. Kingsley. London: Oxford University Press.

Canada. Dept. of Fisheries and Oceans. October 1986. *The Department of Fisheries and Oceans policy for the management of fish habitat*, Ottawa: Canada. Dept. of Fisheries and Oceans.

Canada. Parliament. 1985. *Railway Relocation and Crossing Act, R.S.C. 1985, c. R-4*, Ottawa: Canada. Parliament.

Canada. Parliament. House of Commons. 31 May 1990. *Bill C-73: an act to provide for the dissolution or transfer of certain Crown corporations and to amend certain Acts in consequence thereof*, Ottawa: Canada. Parliament. House of Commons.

Canada. Royal Commission on the Future of the Toronto Waterfront. April 1990. *Environment in transition: a report on phase I of an environmental audit of Toronto's East Bayfront and Port Industrial Area*, Toronto: Canada. Royal Commission on the Future of the Toronto Waterfront.

Canada. Royal Commission on the Future of the Toronto Waterfront. Housing and Neighbourhoods Work Group. 1989. *Housing and neighbourhoods: the liveable waterfront: report on waterfront housing and neighbourhoods to the Royal Commission on the Future of the Toronto Waterfront*. Toronto: Canada. Royal Commmission on the Future of the Toronto Waterfront.

Canada. Royal Commission on the Future of the Toronto Waterfront. 1989. *Interim report: Summer 1989*, Ottawa: Canada. Royal Commission on the Future of the Toronto Waterfront.

Chasan, D. J. and T. J. Dowd. 1988. "Strategic planning: defining port values." In *Urban ports and harbor management: responding to change along U.S. waterfronts*, editor M. J. Hershman. 238. New York: Taylor & Francis.

1990. *Great Lakes, great legacy?*, T. E. Colborn, A. Davidson, S. N. Green, R. A. Hodge, I. C. Jackson, and R. A. Liroff. 230. Baltimore: The Conservation Foundation and the Institute for Research on Public Policy.

Eggleton, A. 9 June 1990. "In Toronto: it's pricey but livable: survey gives us edge over Montreal, five U.S. cities." *Toronto Star* D1.

Erickson, A. 4 October 1980. In *In Erickson's Eden, an architect can improve on nature*, A. Freedman. *Globe and Mail* E3.

Fondersmith, J. March-April 1988. "Downtown 2040: making cities fun." *The futurist* 22(2):12.

Gamble, D. 23 May 1990. "Presentation to the Royal Commission on the Future of the Toronto Waterfront public hearings on environment and health, part II." In *Transcript: public hearings on environment and health, part II*, 112. Toronto: Royal Commission on the Future of the Toronto Waterfront (Canada).

1990. "Habitat restoration." In *RAP revival: a citizens' agenda for RAPs: report from A Remedial Action Plan Workshop for Citizen Leaders, February 9-11, 1990, Stella Niagara, New York*, 14. Buffalo: Great Lakes United.

Hershman, M. J. 1988. "Harbor management: a new role for the public port." In *Urban ports and harbor management: responding to change along U.S. waterfronts*, editor M. J. Hershman. 19. New York: Taylor & Francis.

Hershman, M. J. and R. Scott Bittner. 1988. "Ports over time: historical perspectives on the public port." In *Urban ports and harbor management: responding to change along U.S. waterfronts*, editor M. J. Hershman. 52. New York: Taylor & Francis.

Hilts, S. G. 1986. "Why protect natural heritage?" In *Islands of green: natural heritage protection in Ontario*, 24. Toronto: Ontario Heritage Foundation.

Hiss, T. 21 August 1989. "Reflections: encountering the countryside: II." *New Yorker* 40.

Hough, M. 1989. *City form and natural process: towards a new urban vernacular*, London: Routledge.

_____. 1990. *Out of place: restoring identity to the regional landscape*, New Haven: Yale University Press.

Hough, Stansbury & Woodland Limited, Acrop & Associates, F. J. Reinders and Associates Canada Limited, Michael Michalski Associates, Emrik Suichies & Associates and Anthony Usher Planning Consultant. April 1987. *Port Credit harbour & waterfront concept*, RCFTW Hearing Document, 50004B, Mississauga: Mississauga (Ont.).

International Joint Commission. 1990. *Fifth biennial report under the Great Lakes Water Quality Agreement of 1978 to the governments of the United States and Canada and the state and provincial governments of the Great Lakes Basin: part I*, Ottawa: International Joint Commission.

_____. 1990. *Fifth biennial report under the Great Lakes Water Quality Agreement of 1978 to the governments of the United States and Canada and the state and provincial governments of the Great Lakes Basin: part II*, Ottawa: International Joint Commission.

Irwin, N. A. and F. S. Foreman. March 1990. *Waterfront transportation in the context of regional transportation: background and issues*, Toronto: Canada. Royal Commission on the Future of the Toronto Waterfront.

_____. March 1990. *Waterfront transportation in the context of regional transportation: background and issues: a discussion paper prepared for the Royal Commission on the Future of the Toronto Waterfront*, Toronto: Canada. Royal Commission on the Future of the Toronto Waterfront.

1978. "Isaiah 5:8." In *The holy bible: new international version*, 737. Grand Rapids: Zondervan.

Leopold, A. 1949. "The land ethic." In *A Sand County almanac, and sketches here and there*, 203. Oxford: Oxford University Press.

Marshall, S. 18 April 1990. "Presentation to the Royal Commission on the Future of the Toronto Waterfront public hearings on A Green Strategy for the Greater Toronto Waterfront." *Transcript: public hearings on A Green Strategy for the*

Greater Toronto Waterfront, Toronto: Canada. Royal Commission on the Future of the Toronto Waterfront.

Mayer, H. M. 1988. "The physical harbor: new demands on a scarce resource." In *Urban ports and harbor management: responding to change along U.S. waterfronts*, editor M. J. Hershman. 90. New York: Taylor & Francis.

McCormick Rankin, Macaulay Shiomi Howson Ltd., Gore & Storrie Limited, Stephen Chait Consultants and Tranplan. 6 October 1989. *Draft Shell lands secondary plan*, S.l.: Halton (Ont. : Regional municipality), Burlington (Ont.) and Oakville (Ont.).

Metro Toronto Remedial Action Plan. 11 April 1990. *Draft discussion paper on remedial options*, Toronto: Metro Toronto Remedial Action Plan.

Metro Toronto Remedial Action Plan. Public Advisory Committee. 11 July 1989. *Metro Toronto Remedial Action Plan goals as established by the Public Advisory Committee*, RCFTW Hearing Document, 50027I, Toronto: Metro Toronto Remedial Action Plan. Public Advisory Committee.

Metropolitan Toronto and Region Conservation Authority. July 1989. *The greenspace strategy for the Greater Toronto Region: a conservation vision for the 21st century*, Downsview: Metropolitan Toronto and Region Conservation Authority.

Mississauga (Ont.). Planning and Building Dept. June 1990. *Fundamentals: the basis for the Mississauga Waterfront Plan*, Mississauga: Mississauga (Ont.). Planning and Building Dept.

_____. June 1990. *Strategies to realize the Mississauga Waterfront Plan: implementation: preliminary table of contents*, Mississauga: Mississauga (Ont.). Planning and Building Dept.

_____. June 1990. *Vision 2020: a plan for the Mississauga waterfront*, Mississauga: Mississauga (Ont.). Planning and Building Dept.

Moss, M. L. June 1978. "The urban port: a hidden resource for the city and the coastal zone." In *Urban waterfronts: special issue of Environmental Comment*, 7. Washington: Urban Land Institute.

Mumford, L. 1985. In *Dwellers in the land: the bioregional vision*, K. Sale. 54, 142. San Francisco: Sierra Club.

1985. *The Great Lakes Water Quality Agreement: an evolving instrument for ecosystem management*, National Research Council and Royal Society of Canada. 109. Washington: National Academy Press.

Ontario. April 1989. *Environmental Assessment Act: Revised Statutes of Ontario, 1980, Chapter 140, as amended by 1988, Chapter 71, s. 18: office consolidation*, Toronto: Ontario. Ministry of the Attorney General.

_____. 13 July 1989. *Land use planning for housing: a statement of Ontario government policy issued under the authority of Section 3 of the Planning Act*, Policy statement, Toronto: Ontario. Ministry of Housing and Ontario. Ministry of Municipal Affairs.

_____. August 1989. *Planning Act, 1983. Statutes of Ontario, 1983. Chapter 1 as amended by 1983, chapter 82; 1984, chapter 32, s. 21; and 1985, chapter 16* and 1989, chapter 5 and certain regulations thereunder. Toronto: Ontario. Ministry of the Attorney General.

Ontario Environmental Assessment Advisory Committee. 15 November 1989. *The adequacy of the existing environmental planning and approvals process for the Ganaraska watershed*, Toronto: Ontario Environmental Assessment Advisory Committee.

Ontario. Legislative Assembly. 1989. *Development Charges Act, S.O. 1989, c. 58*, Toronto: Ontario. Legislative Assembly.

Oshawa Harbour Task Force. February 1984. *Oshawa Harbour development plan: a report to the Oshawa Harbour Commission*, Oshawa: Oshawa Harbour Commission.

Pannell Kerr Foster, Patrick Sweet & Associates Limited and Public Management Associates. December 1982. *Land management study for the Port Credit harbour area*, Mississauga: Mississauga (Ont.). Planning and Development Dept.

Parfit, J. 1987. *The health of a city: Oxford, 1770-1974*, Preface. Oxford: Amate Press.

Proctor, Redfern, Bousfield & Bacon. December 1967. *The waterfront plan for the Metropolitan Toronto Planning Area*, Toronto: Metropolitan Toronto (Ont.). Planning Board and Metropolitan Toronto (Ont.). Council.

Rawson Academy of Aquatic Science. September 1989. *Towards an ecosystem charter for the Great Lakes-St. Lawrence*, RCFTW Hearing Document, 50039A, Ottawa: Rawson Academy of Aquatic Science.

Reid, R., R. Lockhart, and B. Woodburn. March 1990. *A green strategy for the Greater Toronto Waterfront: background and issues*, Toronto: Canada. Royal Commission on the Future of the Toronto Waterfront.

Richardson, A. H. 1974. *Conservation by the people: the history of the conservation movement in Ontario to 1970*, xi. Toronto: Conservation Authorities of Ontario.

Sale, K. 1985. *Dwellers in the land: the bioregional vision*, 162. San Francisco: Sierra Club.

Sauriol, C. 1984. *Tales of the Don*, Toronto: Natural Heritage/Natural History Inc.

Schumacher, F. 1985. In *Dwellers in the land: the bioregional vision*, K. Sale. 114. San Francisco: Sierra Club.

Stefansson, V. c. 1930.

Theberge, J. B. 1989. "Changes in water characteristics and aquatic life." In *Legacy: the natural heritage of Ontario*, editor J. B. Theberge. 323. Toronto: McClelland and Stewart.

_____. 1989. "The wholeness of nature." In *Legacy: the natural heritage of Ontario*, editor J. B. Theberge. 375. Toronto: McClelland and Stewart.

Thomas, L. 1985. In *Dwellers in the land: the bioregional vision*, K. Sale. 191. San Francisco: Sierra Club.

Toronto (Ont.). Healthy Toronto 2000 Subcommittee. September 1988. *Healthy Toronto 2000: a strategy for a healthy city*, RCFTW Hearing Document, 50036A, Toronto: Toronto (Ont.) Dept. of Public Health. Healthy Toronto 2000 Subcommittee.

Toronto (Ont.). Planning Board. 18 August 1970. *Metro Centre*, Toronto: Toronto (Ont.). Planning Board.

_____. 20 May 1982. *Plan for the Railway Lands: progress report, Part II*, Toronto: Toronto (Ont.). Planning Board.

_____. 23 January 1978. *The Railway Lands: basis for planning*, Toronto: Toronto (Ont.). Planning Board.

_____. 23 January 1978. *The Railway Lands: proposed goals and objectives*, Toronto: Toronto (Ont.). Planning Board.

Toronto (Ont.). Planning and Development Dept. September 1983. *Railway Lands part II: development concept*. Toronto: Toronto (Ont.). Planning and Development Department.

_____. March 1985. *Railway Lands part II: implementation strategy.* Toronto: Toronto (Ont.) Planning and Development Dept.

_____. August 1985. *Railway Lands part II: memorandum of conditions*, Toronto: Toronto (Ont.). Planning and Development Dept.

Toronto (Ont.). Special Advisory Committee on the Environment. 30 October 1989. *The changing atmosphere: a call to action*, Toronto: Toronto (Ont.). Special Advisory Committee on the Environment.

Toronto Planning Board. 1962. *The core of the Central Waterfront: a proposal by the City of the Toronto Planning Board*, Toronto: Toronto Planning Board.

_____. 1963. *The plan for downtown Toronto*, Toronto: Toronto Planning Board.

APPENDIX C

COMMISSION
PUBLICATIONS

Reports and working papers published by the Royal Commission on the Future of the Toronto Waterfront are available free of charge in both English and French. Publications may be obtained by contacting the Royal Commission on the Future of the Toronto Waterfront, 207 Queen's Quay West, 5th Floor, P.O.Box 4111, Station A, Toronto, Ontario M5W 2V4.

1. *Environment and Health: Issues on the Toronto Waterfront.* Royal Commission on the Future of the Toronto Waterfront. Environment and Health Work Group. ISBN 0-662-16539-2. DSS cat. no. Z1-1988/1-41-1E

2. *Housing and Neighbourhoods: The Liveable Waterfront.* Royal Commission on the Future of the Toronto Waterfront. Housing and Neighbourhoods Work Group. ISBN 0-662-16936-0. DSS cat. no. Z1-1988/1-41-2E

3. *Access and Movement.* Royal Commission on the Future of the Toronto Waterfront. Access and Movement Work Group. ISBN 0-662-16937-9. DSS cat.no. Z1-1988/1-41-3E

4. *Parks, Pleasures, and Public Amenities.* Royal Commission on the Future of the Toronto Waterfront. Parks, Pleasures, and Public Amenities Work Group. ISBN 0-662-16936-0. DSS cat. no. Z1-1988/1-41-4E

5. *Jobs, Opportunities, and Economic Growth.* Royal Commission on the Future of the Toronto Waterfront. Jobs, Opportunities and Economic Growth Work Group. ISBN 0-662-16939-5. DSS cat. no. Z1-1988/1-41-5E

6. *Persistence and Change: Waterfront Issues and the Board of Toronto Harbour Commissioners.* Royal Commission on the Future of the Toronto Waterfront. Steering Committee on Matters Relating to the Board of Toronto Harbour Commissioners. ISBN 0-662-16966-2. DSS cat. no. Z1-1988/1-41-6E

7. *The Future of the Toronto Island Airport: The Issues.* Royal Commission on the Future of the Toronto Waterfront. ISBN 0-662-17067-9. DSS cat. no. Z1-1988/1-41-7E

8. *A Green Strategy for the Greater Toronto Waterfront: Background and Issues.* Ron Reid, Rob Lockhart, and Bob Woodburn. Royal Commission on the Future of the Toronto Waterfront. ISBN 0-662-17671-5. DSS cat. no. Z1-1988/1-41-8E

9. *Waterfront Transportation in the Context of Regional Transportation: Background and Issues.* Neal A. Irwin, and F. Shane Foreman. Royal Commission on the Future of the Toronto Waterfront. ISBN 0-662-17730-4. DSS cat no. Z1-1988/1-52-2E

10. *Environment in Transition: A Report on Phase I of an Environmental Audit of Toronto's East Bayfront and Port Industrial Area.* Royal Commission on the Future of the Toronto Waterfront. ISBN 0-662-17847-5. DSS cat. no. Z1-1988/1-52-3E

Interim Report August 1989. Royal Commission on the Future of the Toronto Waterfront. ISBN 0-662-17215-9. DSS cat. no. Z1-1988/1E

Working Papers

A Selected Bibliography on Toronto's
Port and Waterfront.
CAT Z1-1988/1-42-1E
ISBN 0-662-17596-4

An Index to the First Interim Report.
CAT Z1-1988/1-42-2E
ISBN 0-662-17597-2

Urban Waterfront Industry: Planning
and Developing Green Enterprise for the
21st Century; a Report of the Symposium,
November 16, 1989.
CAT Z1-1988/1-52-1E
ISBN 0-662-17640-5

Soil Contamination and Port
Redevelopment in Toronto.
CAT Z1-1988/1-42-3E
ISBN 0-662-17729-0

The Toronto Harbour Plan of 1912:
Manufacturing Goals and Economic
Realities.
CAT Z1-1988/1-42-4E
ISBN 0-662-18005-4

APPENDIX D

ILLUSTRATION CREDITS

Chapter Two

Chapter Three

p. 130
Lake Shore Road, Toronto, early 1990s
Edwardian postcard, courtesy of the City of
Toronto Archives

p. 133
Farm country in Newcastle
Dr. J.D. Murray

p. 135
*Garden plots on Leslie Street, Port Industrial
Area*
Andrea Short, Royal Commission on the
Future of the Toronto Waterfront

p. 137
*Intergovernmental environmental co-
operation, Audit Progress Report Presen-
tation, February 1990.*
Andrea Short, Royal Commission on the
Future of the Toronto Waterfront

p. 143
Rouge River stream studies
Jim Robb, Save the Rouge Valley System

p. 143
Sixteen Mile Creek at Lions Valley Park
Halton Region Conservation Authority

p. 147
*Controlling water levels with draining,
Centennial Wetland in Scarborough*
Jim Robb, Save the Rouge Valley System

p. 151
Sundown at Ashbridge's Bay
Dr. J.D. Murray

p. 155
Towards Lake Ontario, at Newcastle
Dr. J.D. Murray

Map Credits

Map 1: Greater Toronto Bioregion: 18K
Design Communications, Toronto, Ontario

Map 2: Linking the Green: A Waterfront
Trail: 18K Design Communications, Toronto,
Ontario

Map 3: East Bayfront / Port Industrial Area:
O'Halloran Campbell Consultants Ltd.,
Halifax, Nova Scotia

Exhibition Place / Ontario Place / Fort York
Conceptual Use: Berridge, Lewinberg,
Greenberg, Toronto, Ontario

Artwork

Oak Ridges Moraine Poster: Save The Oak
Ridges Moraine, Richmond Hill, Ontario.

INDEX

A

B

C

D

Etobicoke Creek (Etobicoke, Ont.), 35, 112

Etobicoke Motel Strip. *See* Motel Strip (Etobicoke, Ont.)

Etobicoke (Ont.), 60, 65, 113-118

Etobicoke (Ont.). City Council, 95, 113-114, 118-119

eutrophication, 18, 51-52

Exhibition Place (Toronto, Ont.), 72, 97, 120, 123, 126-128

federal government, 33, 41, 59, 83-85, 92, 94-95, 110, 112, 127, 129-132, 136, 138, 146, 154-155

federal lands, 83-84, 112, 129, 134, 154

Federal Nut and Bolt, 118

Federal Water Policy, 96

Federation of Ontario Naturalists, 55, 85

festivals, 126, 128

Fifth Biennial Report under the Great Lakes Water Quality Agreement of 1978, 84, 90

financial districts, 120, 129, 134

fish, 18-19, 23-24, 27, 35-36, 42-45, 51-52, 54, 76, 88, 98

fish stocking, 99

fisheries, 18-19, 43, 55, 112. *See also* sport fisheries

flooding, 31, 102-103, 110, 112, 153

flying squirrel, 45

FON *See* Federation of Ontario Naturalists

Food Products building (Exhibition Place, Toronto, Ont.), 127

Fort York (Toronto, Ont.), 120, 123-124, 128

Forty Bay St. (Toronto, Ont.). *See* 40 Bay St. (Toronto, Ont.)

Fourteen Mile Creek (Hamilton, Ont.), 57, 110

Frenchman's Bay (Pickering, Ont.), 56, 153

Front St. (Toronto, Ont.), 131

Fundamentals: The Basis for the Mississauga Waterfront Plan, 111

funding, 85, 94-95, 103, 107, 110-112, 116-117, 124, 128, 148-150, 153

Ganaraska Region Conservation Authority, 150

Ganaraska River (Ont.), 88

Ganaraska Trail (Ont.), 86

Ganaraska Valley (Ont.), 86

garbage. *See* solid waste

Gardiner Expressway (Toronto, Ont.), 70-72, 120, 122, 132, 135

Humber Bay (Etobicoke, Ont.), 115

Humber River (Etobicoke, Ont.), 72, 87, 115

Humber River Watershed, 95

Humber Sewage Treatment Plant, 115-116

Hyde Park (London, England), 124

IJC. *See* International Joint Commission

Improved Lakefill Quality Control Program, 97

income tax, 28

industrialization, 24

industry, 28, 31, 52, 59-60, 117-118, 138, 142, 151. *See also* environmentally friendly industry

intergovernmental co-operation, 33, 35, 37, 47, 72, 83, 91, 95, 99, 119, 131, 136-137, 145, 155

Interim Report, 1989, 83, 94, 96, 106, 117, 128, 136, 138, 147

International Joint Commission, 33, 35, 37, 83, 90-94, 115

International Trade Centre, 127-128

interpretive centres, 76, 87

intervenor funding, 116-117

investment, 123-124, 128

Izzard, Dorothy, 89

J. C. Saddington Park (Mississauga, Ont.), 111

Javits Center (New York, N. Y.), 127

Johns-Manville site (Scarborough, Ont.), 146, 149

Joshua Creek (Oakville, Ont.), 56, 112

jurisdiction, 46-47, 83-85, 90, 95, 124, 136, 145, 151

Kanter, Ron, 89, 103-104

Kew Beach Residents Association, 53

King Business Centre, 124, 127

Kingston Rd. (Toronto, Ont.), 146

Klinger, Xenia, 62

Lake Erie, 18-19

Lake Ontario, 21-25, 31, 33, 37-38, 42, 44, 58, 72, 84, 91-92, 100, 106-107

M

mixed use, 59, 63, 65, 76, 79, 111, 114, 144

MNR. *See* Ontario. Ministry of Natural Resources

model sewer use by-law, 84, 93. *See also* sewage treatment

MOE. *See* Ontario. Ministry of the Environment

Molson site (Toronto, Ont.), 120, 124, 129

Moore, Richard, 78

moratoria, 97-98, 119

MOT. *See* Ontario. Ministry of Transportation

Motel Strip (Etobicoke, Ont.), 66, 109, 114-117

Motel Strip Secondary Plan, 113-115

MTRCA. *See* Metropolitan Toronto and Region Conservation Authority

municipal government, 58, 66, 83, 85, 88-89, 92, 96, 99, 101, 104, 150, 152

Municipal-Industrial Strategy for Abatement, 36, 92

Municipal-Industrial Strategy for Abatement. Sewer Use Control Program, 1994, 93

Municipality of Metropolitan Toronto. *See* Metropolitan Toronto (Ont.)

museums, 129

Music Building (Exhibition Place, Toronto, Ont.), 123

muskellunge, 42-43

N

National Research Council of Canada, 143

native species, 55, 99-101

natural areas, 54-57, 64-65, 78, 87, 90, 102, 108, 120, 152. *See also* wilderness areas

natural heritage, 63, 72, 84, 86

Natural Sciences and Engineering Research Council Canada, 143

nautical centres, 129

Neptune Meters Canada Limited, 118

Newcastle (Ont.), 107, 154

Newcastle (Ont.). Town Council, 150

Niagara Escarpment (Ont.), 22, 24, 88

Niagara Peninsula (Ont.), 106-107

Niagara River, 91

Nodal concept, 104

North Toronto Sewage Treatment Plant, 37

Noxell (Canada) Corporation, 118

Noxzema company. *See* Noxell (Canada) Corporation

NSERC. *See* Natural Sciences and Engineering Research Council Canada

Oak Ridges Moraine (Ont.), 22, 24, 36-37, 45, 72-73, 86, 88-90, 103-106

Oakville Harbour, 107, 110

Oakville (Ont.), 87, 107, 110

Oakville (Ont.). Town Council, 66, 108-109

Official Plan Part II: Railway Lands, 134

official plans, 58, 84, 88, 107, 112-113, 119, 129, 133, 148-150, 152

Olympic Games, 128

Olympic Stadium (Toronto, Ont.), 126, 128

OMB. *See* Ontario Municipal Board

Ontario. Minister of Municipal Affairs and Housing, 104, 119

Ontario. Minister of the Environment, 117

Ontario. Ministry of Industry, Trade and Technology, 143

Ontario. Ministry of Natural Resources, 55, 99, 103, 153

Ontario. Ministry of the Environment, 35, 41, 44, 92, 115, 143

Ontario. Ministry of Transportation, 110

Ontario Environmental Assessment Advisory Committee, 88-89, 115

Ontario Government Building (Exhibition Place, Toronto, Ont.), 123

Ontario Hydro, 110, 112, 153

Ontario Jockey Club, 145-146

Ontario Municipal Board, 115, 116, 132, 134

Ontario Place (Toronto, Ont.), 97, 120, 123-124, 126-128

Ontario Research Foundation. *See* ORTECH INTERNATIONAL

Ontario Wildlife Working Group, 98

open space, 46, 62-66, 68, 84, 86, 103, 108-110, 115, 146, 148, 150

ORTECH INTERNATIONAL, 143

Oshawa Creek (Oshawa, Ont.), 72, 153

Oshawa Creek valley, 150

Oshawa Harbour Commission, 150, 154

Oshawa Harbour Development Plan: A Report to the Oshawa Harbour Commission, 154

Oshawa (Ont.), 59, 68, 86, 106

Oshawa (Ont.) City Council, 57, 150, 154

Oshawa Second Marsh, 56-57, 150, 153

Outer Harbour Marina (Toronto, Ont.), 140

Outer Harbour Sailing Federation, 77, 140

ozone, 39-41

P

S

U

V

W

wood turtle, 43, 53

Woodbine Ave. (Toronto, Ont.), 145-146

World Trade Centre (Toronto, Ont.), 141

Y

York (Ont.), 22, 88, 93

York (Ont.). City Council, 32

York (Ont.: Regional municipality), 37

Z

zebra mussel, 23, 45

Zeidler, Eberhard, 129

Zero Discharge, 33, 91

zoning, 112, 118, 133-134, 146